An Easy Cou███████████████ l
Programming ɯne HP 48G/GX

by Chris Coffin

Illustrations by Robert L. Bloch

Grapevine Publications, Inc.

P.O. Box 2449

Corvallis, Oregon 97339-2449 U.S.A.

Acknowledgments

The term "48" is used for convenience herein to refer to the HP 48GX and the HP 48G, the registered trade names for the handheld calculator/computer products of Hewlett-Packard Co. We extend our thanks once again to Hewlett-Packard for their top-quality products and documentation.

Printed in the United States of America
ISBN 0-931011-41-8

Third Printing – August, 1996

CONTENTS

0 **START HERE**

What Is This Machine?

Before you start using your HP 48G or HP 48GX (call it simply "48" for short), here's some idea of what you can expect: The 48 is a calculator—a tool to give you quick answers to quick questions. Most often this means keying in a value or two, pressing a key, and reading the result in the display.

The 48 is designed to work in just that way. Although it's very sophisticated, *most of its operations are just variations on that basic theme*: Ask-A-Question/Get-An-Answer. If you keep this in mind, you'll get along very well.

One more thought: The 48 is a *tool,* designed to be used in a certain way for certain things. It's a great general-purpose calculating tool, but it's not the best tool for every job. When it's easier to use pencil and paper —or a larger computer—do it! Always choose the right tool for the job.

What Is This Book?

This book is *not* a reference manual (HP already did their usual great job on that). It's *not* an intensely in-depth treatment of programming, equation-solving, or *any* of the many things you can do "in-depth" on the 48. There are simply not enough pages in one book to do all that.

This book *is* a tutorial *introductory* course on the 48—a step-by-step, self-pacing course to orient you and get you "up-to-speed" on many features of the machine—*so that you can then use the HP manuals more profitably as you continue to practice with your 48.*

The [ON] Key

From the looks of the keyboard, there's a lot to learn about this machine; each key has several meanings. So although the [ON] key may seem a trivial a place to start...

Do This: Turn on your 48 by pressing the [ON] key at the lower left. Now turn it off, by pressing [→][OFF]. Notice the different function names printed on or around the [ON] key. The functions are related to one another, but the one you get depends on whether you press one of the shift keys first. This is the case with most keys on the machine.

Adjusting the Display

Next, make sure that you can read the display comfortably.

Do This: With the machine turned on, press *and hold down* the [ON] key, then press either the [+] or [−] key until the display adjusts to a comfortable viewing angle.

You can do this at any time. And—like most of its modes and settings—the calculator will remember and use this viewing angle until you change it.

Setting the Machine for this Course

There's one other thing to do before beginning with the actual Course. You may not yet know what this is all about—but don't worry: This is the one time when it's all right simply to press buttons without trying to understand what you're doing. This procedure is just to be sure that _your_ machine has the settings this Course assumes....

Do This: Type: ⬅CLEAR MTH ⬅{} ➡#0 ➡#0 ENTER. Again, notice how you must press the purple ⬅ or the green ➡ to activate a keyboard function of that color.

Then α α S T O F ENTER 1 6 +/− SPC α S α F ➡HOME ➡POLAR (the alphabetic characters are printed in white at the lower right of the keys). Now your display should look like this:*

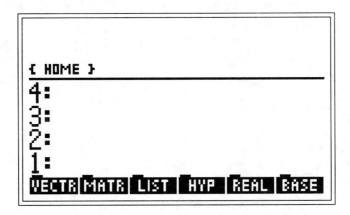

```
{ HOME }
_____
4:
3:
2:
1:
VECTR MATR LIST HYP REAL BASE
```

That's it—you're finished with the preparations. Now, on with the Course....

*If your display looks different, just repeat this entire procedure.

☐1 YOUR 48 WORKSHOP

Calculating with Tools and Objects

Once upon a time, working with a calculator meant just using numbers and doing math. You could calculate lengths and angles in geometry, and distances, areas, rates, logarithms and roots—to 10-digit accuracy.

But that's not enough anymore. Now engineers, scientists and technicians from all sorts of disciplines expect a calculator to deal with complex numbers, vectors, matrices, tables of data, etc. And nearly everybody uses some kind of electronic note pad or text storage nowadays.

So, *wouldn't it be nice* to have a calculator that worked with these more sophisticated data types *in the same way* that your old calculator worked with numbers?   (...yep—you guessed it....)

How the 48 Does It

One unifying idea now emerging in computers is that data are simply "things"—*objects* on which you perform work. And functions or programs are the *tools* with which you do this work. In the expression $2 + 3$, for example, the numbers 2 and 3 are simply objects that you combine to form a new object (5), using the + tool—just as you combine two blocks of wood to form a new object, using a hammer.

And now this idea of a *tool* (+) can apply to more than just real numbers. It works the same, whether you're adding real numbers, complex numbers or vectors. The results are different, because you start with different "materials," but the tool you use is the same—*so the 48 lets you use the same simple keystroke* (⊞) in each case.

The Big Picture: A Workshop

The 48 is a collection of *materials* (objects) and the *tools* to use on them (operations, etc.). So it's really a calculations *workshop:*

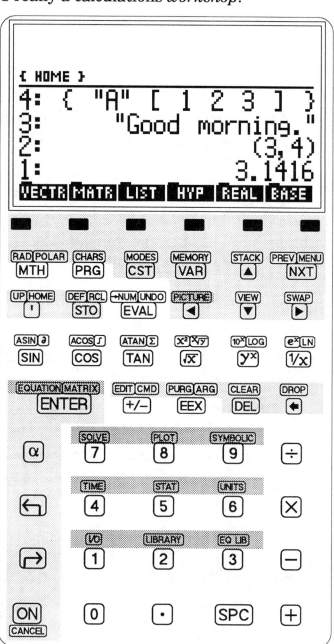

The Stack is the "workbench" in your workshop—where you literally "stack up" objects to use or combine. Most of this combining happens at the *bottom* of the Stack, so those bottom Levels are generally shown in the display.

Some keys simply help you control, move around and operate in the workshop—store and retrieve objects, get tools, rearrange the workbench, set modes, etc.

The rest of the keys are mostly "hand tools." That is, they are functions, within your easy reach at the workbench, that perform simple operations on objects on the Stack. The most commonly used hand tools (along with their inverses) have their own keys, but many others are gathered in "toolboxes"—*collections* of items you use via *menus* in the display—like the MaTH menu you see in the display here.

The "power tools" are smart, specialized tools that help you build, view or "crunch" sophisticated objects more conveniently.

As you work in the workshop, *you create your own storage compartments* for the objects you build (the objects shown below are just examples—these are not stored in your machine). The storage compartments are *directories*.

You can create directories *even within other* directories. And each directory has a *path* from the **HOME** (uppermost) directory—the route you must take to reach it. The path of the *current* directory (i.e. "where you are" right now) shows at the top of the display within **{ }**.

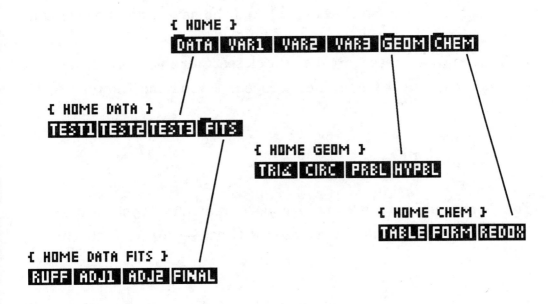

The (VAR) key shows you the menu of all the objects ("VARiables") you have stored in the current directory.

The Display: Your Window into the Workshop

To see into your workshop, turn on your 48 and look at the display....

The Stack

Look at the space *between* the horizontal line near the top of the display and the row of boxes at the very bottom (if you don't see these things, press CANCEL—the ON key). This is the Stack—the actual "workbench" where you place the materials you're using. It's called a Stack because that's how objects "sit" on the workbench: The object *nearest to you* is at the *bottom* of the Stack (Level 1); and the next nearest object is at Level 2, etc. You may not see many more objects stacked up above that (in fact you'll never see more than the closest four objects), *but there can be hundreds more up there*. They reappear as you remove lower objects.

The Command Line

The Command Line is a *temporary space* created to let you gather your materials *before* putting them onto the Stack—your work bench.

Do This: Type a number—say, 14 (press 1 4).... See how the Stack lines move up to make room for what you type? That 14 is *not* on the Stack—it's on the Command Line—until you actually put it onto the Stack, by pressing ENTER, or throw it away via CANCEL (ON). Throw it away now: CANCEL.

The Menu Line

At the very bottom of the display is the Menu Line. A menu is simply a convenient *collection* of related tools—a "toolbox," if you will. For although the crowded 48 keyboard already offers many tools "within your immediate reach," there are hundreds more stored in menus— even in menus *within* menus.

So, in making a selection from a menu, you are selecting a tool or opening another toolbox (menu). And it's easy: To make a selection from a menu, you just press the white key directly beneath it.

The Status Area

Now look at the display above the horizontal line. Here sits a set of warning lights and messages above your work bench—signs that light up to announce events or warn you of problems.

In a real workshop you might see "Power On" lights and "Saw Jammed" signs. On the 48, you'll see warning messages telling you, in effect: "You just tried to use a tool on the empty benchtop!" or "You can't use that tool on that object." And you'll see "indicator lights" that tell you when certain tools will operate differently because you've turned on an optional *mode*.

So be sure to watch the Status Area! Mode indicators stay on as long as the mode is active, but warning signs appear only temporarily; they turn off the next time you press a key.*

---

*Therefore, to further attract your attention to these warnings, the 48 usually beeps at you, too.

The Keyboard: Access to Your Workshop

The keyboard is how you make things happen in your workshop—putting objects on the workbench, using tools, moving around, etc.

The Shift Keys

The colored keys, ⬅ ("left-shift") and ➡ ("right-shift"), indeed shift the meanings of keys to the colored functions printed above them. Also, a *mode indicator* appears in the Status Area when a "shift" is in effect). Notice that shift keys are *toggle keys:* If a "shift" is on, pressing that shift key turns it *off*—and vice versa.

The Numeric Keys

Often the objects on your workbench are numbers, so the numeric keys and [+], [−], [×], [÷], [ENTER], [+/−], and [EEX] are all grouped together for your "calculating convenience."

The Alphabetic Keys

The [α] key is really another shift key: You press it prior to another key to get that key's *alphabetic* function (shown in *white* to the lower right). The Status Area will then show a α indicator. Notice that you can *lock* alpha mode on by pressing [α] a second time; the third time turns it off, so [α] is a *3*-way toggle key. And you can use ⬅ and ➡ *within* alpha mode; each key can have 3 *primary* meanings and 3 *alpha* meanings.

Selecting: Menu Keys and Input Forms

The six blank white keys directly under the display are the menu keys. Menus appear in the display, and you make selections with these keys.

Try It: Press ⬅(MODES)**ANGL**. This menu is where you can set the machine's angle modes (options). As with most menus, there are more than six selections here, though. Use (NXT) (to see the NeXT page) or ⬅(PREV) (the PREVious page).... This menu has just two pages (and the second page has just one item—an easy way to return to the MODES menu). Move to the menu page that looks something like this:

DEG ▪| RAD | GRAD |RECT▪|CYLIN|SPHER

The little boxes in the **DEG ▪** and **RECT▪** selections tell you that those modes are now set (DEGree angle mode and RECTangular vector mode). But press the menu key under **RAD** .... The menu and the Status Area tell you that the machine is now in RADians angle mode. Try other items on this menu page if you wish (but when you're finished, leave the modes as you found them—as shown above).

In many areas of the 48, you can control it in *two different ways*:

(i) through a *menu*—via the unlabeled ⬅ (left-shifted) key;

(ii) through an *input form*—via the labelled ➡ (right-shifted) key.

Thus, ⬅(MODES) (as you just did, above) gave you the MODES menu; but ➡(MODES) will give you the MODES input form....

Try It: Press →[MODES]. You'll see this:

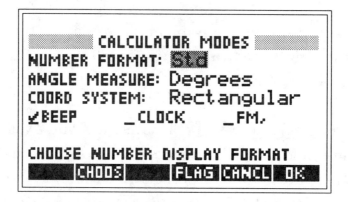

The general rules for input forms are:

- The *highlighted field* is the one you can change (e.g. the **NUMBER FORMAT** field above)—the line just above the menu will remind you with a prompt. To move the highlight, use ▲, ▼, ▶ and ◀.

- The **CHOOS** item on the menu offers you a message box from which you can make a highlighted selection (again, use the arrow keys to move the highlight).

- For fields such as **_BEEP** or **_CLOCK**, a **✔CHK** menu item appears when you highlight that field. It is a *toggle*: use it either to check or uncheck the field.

- [ENTER] or **OK** will accept your selection; **CANCL** will cancel it.

Experiment with this form. Keep in mind that you'll find many such input forms on the 48, and they all work similarly.

When you're finished, leave the modes as shown above, return to a normal Stack display (via [CANCEL], [ENTER] or **OK**). Then press [MTH].

The Tools in Your Workshop

Hand Tools

Usually with the 48 , you create a simple object and select a simple, one-step tool to use on it—like putting a board onto the workbench and using a hammer to drive a nail into it. The drawers and toolboxes (*menus*) in your 48 workshop are full of such simple, one-step tools. You must simply learn when to use them—and how.

Power Tools

Sometimes simple tools aren't enough. To build, use, or make major changes to a sophisticated object (and be guided through the process) you need *power tools*—instruments and analyzers that perform more complex manipulations. For example, to create a table of numbers (an array)—4 rows of 5 columns, you *could* type the whole thing into the Command Line; or, you could use the MATRIX editor power tool, which presents you with a template that you can fill and edit more easily.

Other power tools let you build, solve or plot equations, manage time, do statistics, etc. These are all *smart* tools; they know something about the materials you're using and thus can eliminate much of the simple-minded work. So instead of a tool that "nails this piece to that," you have a tool that "makes a chair," or "designs a beam to support a 1-ton load." In this way, power tools actually augment your knowledge, by *automatically performing sophisticated operations* whose details would otherwise cost you time to learn or recall, and then execute one-by-one.

The Raw Materials in Your Workshop

With all the hundreds of *tools* in your 48 workshop, you have just a few basic types of *materials* (objects) with which to build. *Each type looks different* so that you can distinguish it from the others:

Real Numbers

On the 48, real numbers look and act like what you normally think of as numbers: `3    15    10000    -0.9    -50.2        3.14`

Units

Units are real numbers with *dimensions*. That is, you can use real numbers to represent physical quantities (i.e., feet, pounds, psi, liters, etc.), by assigning them units—and these units will be used correctly throughout any calculations you perform. Here are some numbers with units: `1_ft      17.3_kPa      9.81_m/s^2`.
Note the *underscore* (_) that connects the number to its units.

Complex Numbers

A complex number is a vector—an ordered pair—in the complex plane. The 48 represents a *rectangular* complex number as two real numbers (real, imaginary), like this: `(3, 4)`. Or, that same number can also appear in *polar* form, with a magnitude and an angle: `(5, ∡53.13)`. The angle may be in degrees, radians or grads.

Arrays

An array is a group of numbers (either real or complex numbers), with no set limit on the size of the group, as long as it's arranged in a *table* of rows and columns—which can then be used mathematically as a *matrix*. The 48 represents arrays *within brackets*:

```
[[ 1 2 ]          [[ 1 2 3 ]]          [[ 1 ]
 [ 3 4 ]]                               [ 2 ]]
```
  2x2 array   1-row array   1-column array

               (row-vector)   (column-vector)

Flags

Flags are the simplest object type of all—*bits*—objects with only two possible values: 1 or 0 (on or off, set or clear—whatever)—usually to signal a mode or condition. Flags don't appear individually on the Stack, but you can set or test them individually or as groups.

Binary Integers

Binary integers are just that—integers made up of binary digits—bits (i.e. flags). You can do binary arithmetic on them and use them to represent *groups* of flags. The 48 displays binary integers on the Stack, not only in binary form (base 2) but also in number bases 8, 10 and 16. For example, 1011_2 appears as # 1011b 307_8 appears as # 307o

                 43_{10} appears as # 43d $A7F_{16}$ appears as # A7Fh

The # indicates a binary integer; the b, o, d, or h suffix tells you the base (binary, octal, decimal, hexadecimal).

Character Strings

On the 48, you build character *strings*—sets of characters linked together to form objects—words or sentences of verbal information, *denoted by quotation marks:* `"Hi!"` `"Phone home."`   `"1+1=2"`

Tags

Tags are temporary labels for objects on the workbench (the Stack)—like masking tape. A tag labels an object with an *identifier and a colon to its left:*   `Answer: 17`   `Altitude: 29000`   `RANGE: 10`

Names

Names are words that identify things. On the 48, you use names to identify storage locations. The name is the *label* you tape onto the *storage location* to identify what's in it (you don't name an object itself). A 48 name is *a single word within apostrophes:* `'HUBERT'` `'Wrench'`

Algebraic Objects

Algebraic objects look and behave like algebraic expressions and equations. On the 48, you type them *between apostrophes*—just like names, except that algebraic objects can contain mathematical operations and functions not allowed in names:

   `'A+B=C'`   `'SIN(x)'`   `'pi*RADIUS^2'`

Programs

A program is a *custom-built* tool—a series of instructions (objects and tools) strung together, to be executed at a later time. You create a program, then name it (i.e., store it in a named toolbox). And then you have a new tool to use—just as you would use any other tool in the workshop. 48 programs are enclosed in « », like this:

« 1 2 + »   « "Hi" BEEP CLEAR »

Lists

Lists are *collections* of objects, the wire and glue of your workshop that binds together objects of *any types*—even other lists—within *braces:*

{ 1 2 3 }   { "Hi" 7 (3,4) "Bye" }

Directories

Directories are the *storage areas* you create for your objects. They appear as menu items with small "index tabs:"

DATA GEOM CHEM FITS

There are other, more obscure object types on the 48, but these are the basic raw materials you'll be working with most often.

Look Again at the Workshop

Holding your place here, look back again at the Big Picture of your 48 workshop (page 14)....

Gradually, now, the maze of names and keys on your machine should be emerging into some kind of coherent picture of what you're working with here:

- You have a very sophisticated calculator—one that allows you to _operate on_ (i.e. build, edit, combine) not only numbers but many other types of objects.

- When performing these operations, you generally place these objects on your workbench—the Stack.

- You perform the operations themselves with commands that are available on keys or via menus. Most of these commands do simple things; they are "hand tools." A certain few are smarter and more complex—the "power tools."

- You name and store your created objects in directories that you create.

Conceptually, it's pretty simple, no? Be sure to keep this "Big Picture" in mind as you start to learn the details. Test yourself now....

Quiz on the "Big Picture"

At the end of every chapter this Course gives you a quiz, to make sure you're "digesting" what you read. These quizzes aren't trivial—they're a big part of your learning process—so don't breeze over them; think and apply your knowledge! The solutions immediately follow the questions, so study them and re-read parts of the chapter, as necessary.

1. What sorts of problems do you expect to solve with the 48?

2. Why use a workshop analogy when describing the 48?

3. How many keys would the 48 need if it didn't have the α, ⇐ and ⇒ keys?

4. What's a menu? What's an input form? Why does the 48 use them? What are the advantages of each?

5. What's a real number (as represented on the 48)?

6. What's an array (as represented on the 48)?

7. What's a power tool (on the 48)? Name three of them.

Quiz Answers

1. You can expect to solve most kinds of number-crunching and data-intensive problems. Some may be intricate and require special programming, but for most you will key in some values, press a function key, and get an answer. The 48 has a vast supply of functions—and the flexibility to allow you to create your own.

2. The workshop analogy is good because the 48 uses *tools* (functions and operations) on *raw materials* (data objects—real numbers, arrays, lists, etc.). The Stack acts much like a workbench, too; it's where most of the building and crunching happens.

3. It would need about six times as many as it has now. The [α], [←] and [→] keys allow most keys to "mean" six different things.

4. The 48 uses menus to avoid the need for even more keys: A menu is a selection of items that appears in the display. To select from a menu, press the blank white key beneath that selection.

    For many purposes, the 48 also offers input forms—"fill-in-the-blank" screens which are more explanatory and which prompt you and show you your options for each field on the screen.

    In general, the trade-off between menus and input forms is that input forms are "friendlier" but menus are often faster.

5. On the 48, real numbers are what you usually think of as real numbers: 1   15   -1000   0.3   -50   3.1416

6. On the 48, arrays are groups of numbers—either real or complex number—arranged in rows and columns and represented *within brackets*:

[[1 2]
  [3 4]]
	[[1 2 3]]	[[1]
		  [2]]

2×2 array	1-row array (row-vector)	1-column array (column-vector)

7. A power tool is a smart, specialized tool that helps you build, view or "crunch" sophisticated objects more conveniently. Where your simpler "hand tools" are like saws and hammers, your power tools are more like lathes and drill presses. They are: [PICTURE], [EQUATION], [MATRIX], [SOLVE], [PLOT], [SYMBOLIC], [TIME], [STAT], and [UNITS].

[2] THE STACK AND COMMAND LINE:
YOUR WORKBENCH

Typing and the Command Line

It's time to start learning how to work at your workbench....

To Begin: Press the digit keys ([0] through [9]) in sequence and look at the display. You should see something like this:*

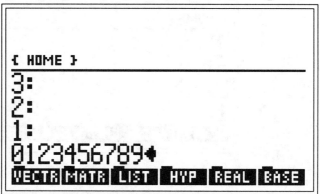

A space opens up between the workbench itself (the Stack) and the Menu Line. And what you just typed has been placed in this space, which is the *Command Line.*

The number you've typed is *not yet* on the workbench; it's still an *unfinished* command. To finish it—and to officially place the object onto the workbench—you must press [ENTER]. Do that now....

See? The Command Line disappears and the object, as the 48 has interpreted it, is placed on Level 1—that's the *bottom,* the nearest Level to you—on your workbench.

---

*If your display isn't exactly like this, don't worry too much. At this point you're most concerned with that number you just typed in. If it's just the menu line that's different, press [MTH].

So that's how to type in a real number and put it onto the workbench. Now, what about something that's not a number?

Do This: Press ⓐ....

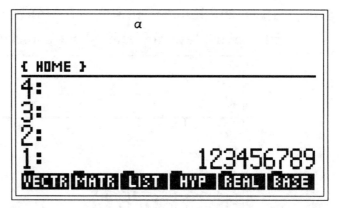

Notice the α that appears now in the Status Area, telling you that the next key you press will return its alphabetic character; you are in *alpha mode*.

Continue: Press ⒶⓐⒷⓐⒸ. ABC♦ appears on the Command Line— and notice that you had to press ⓐ before *every* letter.

Now press CANCEL (that's the ON key).

What happened?

The ABC that you had typed on the Command Line was not put onto the workbench. It was *thrown away*.

That's what CANCEL does: it tells the calculator to cancel whatever was "in progress."

Now try typing something a little more complicated.

Press: $\boxed{\alpha}\boxed{\alpha}\boxed{W}\boxed{H}\boxed{A}\boxed{T}\boxed{SPC}\boxed{Y}\boxed{O}\boxed{U}\boxed{SPC}\boxed{S}\boxed{E}\boxed{E}\boxed{SPC}\boxed{I}\boxed{S}\boxed{SPC}\boxed{W}\boxed{H}\boxed{A}\boxed{T}$
$\boxed{SPC}\boxed{Y}\boxed{O}\boxed{U}\boxed{SPC}\boxed{G}\boxed{E}\boxed{T}\boxed{\cdot}\boxed{\alpha}$

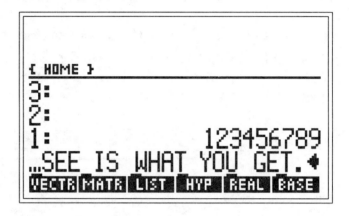

See how you can save a lot of keystrokes by using "alpha-lock" (pressing $\boxed{\alpha}$ twice in a row), so that the alpha annunciator stays on?

Notice also that the first part of what you typed is now pushed off the left-hand side of the display. The ... on the left tells you that the Command Line extends off that side of the display. To see what's missing, press $\boxed{\triangleleft}$ repeatedly (or press it and hold it) until the 48 beeps to tell you "there ain't no more."

Notice that you couldn't do this if you hadn't switched back out of alpha mode with the final $\boxed{\alpha}$, above. In alpha mode, the $\boxed{\triangleleft}$ key is something entirely different—the $\boxed{P}$ key. So you can see that it's important to know what mode you're working in—watch your Status Area!

Inserting and Deleting Characters

Next question: How do you correct mistakes and make amendments to your typing on the Command Line?

Do This: Using ◄ and ►, move the cursor so that it's on top of the S in SEE. Then type ⓐⓐⒸⒶⓃ(SPC)ⓐ.

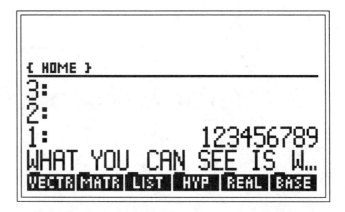

The new characters are *inserted*; this is how you add to what's already in the Command Line.

And it's just as easy to *remove* characters. For example, to remove the CAN that you just inserted...

Do This: Press ←←←←. Notice how ← deletes the character *before* the cursor.

You could have used the DEL (delete) key, also—but it deletes the character *under* the cursor (not to its left), so you would have had to move the cursor. Press DEL once now, to delete the S in SEE.

Lower-Case Letters

Try This: Type: [CANCEL] [α][α] [H][←][I] [SPC] [←][T] [←][H] [←][E] [←][R] [←][E] [·][α]. Nothing to it—you get lower-case by using [←] before each letter! But it's a lot of extra typing, so...

Notice: [CANCEL][α][α] [H] [←][α] [I][SPC][T][H][E][R][E][·][α]. Pressing [←][α] *when you're already in alpha mode* will *lock* the 48 into lower-case mode. And it will stay in effect until you leave the Command Line or press [←][α] again.

Special Characters

There are lots of *non-alphabetic* characters (things other than A–z) available on the 48. Most are *right-shifted* ([→]) alphabet keys, for which HP offers you some built-in help via the [→][CHARS] key (try it now).... This screen shows you 64 characters at a time (select a different 64 via the **-64** and **+64**). The display shows you the key to get the highlighted character (use the arrow keys to move the highlight)—or **ECHO** will also put the character on the Command Line for you.

Note that certain characters, called *delimiters*, are indeed marked on keys, because they denote certain object types. For example, [ꞌ] gives you ꞌ ꞌ (and the ◆ points between them)—because you'll usually want to *enclose* the object you're typing with these apostrophes. The other delimiter characters that come in pairs are on the shifted arithmetic keys [←][( )], [←][[ ]], [←][« »], [→][" "], [←][{ }], and [→][: :].

The ⟨→⟩⟨↵⟩ (_NEWLINE_) Key

The Command Line is actually a space—not a line. It can be broken up into more than one line by using ⟨→⟩⟨↵⟩ (right-shifted ⟨·⟩)—the NEWLINE key.

Try This: Type ⟨CANCEL⟩⟨α⟩⟨α⟩ ⟨M⟩⟨O⟩⟨R⟩⟨E⟩ ⟨→⟩⟨↵⟩ ⟨T⟩⟨H⟩⟨A⟩⟨N⟩ ⟨→⟩⟨↵⟩ ⟨O⟩⟨N⟩⟨E⟩ ⟨→⟩⟨↵⟩⟨L⟩⟨I⟩⟨N⟩⟨E⟩⟨→⟩⟨↵⟩⟨←⟩⟨I⟩ (that's ⟨←⟩⟨DEL⟩)⟨α⟩.

You now have _five_ lines in the Command "Line." The first line has scrolled off the top of the display, but it's still there.

Notice also that when you have more than one line like this, ⟨▲⟩ and ⟨▼⟩ move the cursor from line to line up and down—just as ⟨◀⟩ and ⟨▶⟩ move you around to edit a single-line Command Line.

Not only that, ⟨→⟩⟨◀⟩ and ⟨→⟩⟨▶⟩ will move you to the first and last characters of a line, and ⟨→⟩⟨▲⟩ and ⟨→⟩⟨▼⟩ will move you to the first and last lines.

Spend a little time now and play with this....

Then, without leaving your current Command "Line" (that multi-line thing), read on....

The EDIT Toolbox

Not all your Command Line editing tools are available on their own keys. With so many tools, the 48 has most of them stored in toolboxes (menus)—including a set of tools for editing the Command Line. You can open that toolbox with the ←(EDIT) key.

Try It: Press ←(EDIT) to see this menu of the items in that toolbox:

◄SKIP   SKIP►   ◄DEL   DEL►   INS □   ↑STK

◄SKIP and **SKIP►** move the cursor in the indicated directions (similar to ◄ and ►), but they move until they encounter a space (or NEWLINE) and then stop at the next character. Try **◄SKIP** and **SKIP►** now and watch how the cursor moves.

◄DEL and **DEL►** work the same way as **◄SKIP** and **SKIP►**, except that instead of *skipping over* those characters, they *delete* them.

INS □ is a *mode* key (remember the **RAD □** key on the MODES menu?) The **INS □** key *changes the form of cursor* in the Command Line: When the □ appears to the right of **INS**, the calculator is in *insert* mode; the cursor is ◄, and newly typed characters are *inserted* to its left.

But press **INS □** now.... Notice that it becomes **INS ■**, and that the ◄ becomes a ■. The 48 is now in *replace* mode; a newly typed character will *replace* the character under the cursor.

Now press (CANCEL) to throw away the current Command Line.

Next: Press ⑤ (ENTER) ④ ③ (ENTER). You should now see this:

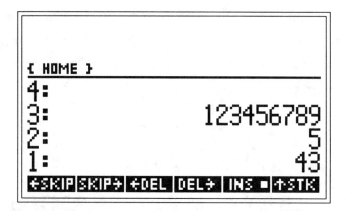

Then: Begin a new Command Line. Type: α α ① (SPC) Ⓐ Ⓜ (SPC)(SPC) Ⓨ Ⓔ Ⓐ Ⓡ Ⓢ (SPC) Ⓞ Ⓛ Ⓓ · α. Next, use ◄SKIP ◄SKIP ◄ to move the insert cursor here: **AM ◆YEARS**, then press **↑STK**:

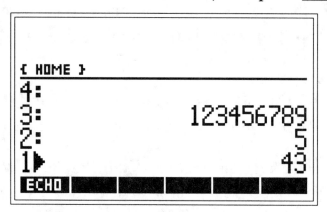

Now *ECHO* (i.e. copy) an object (the 5) from the Stack to the Command Line: Press ▲ once to move the pointer up a Level. Then press **ECHO** once, then (ENTER) to return to the Command Line.... See how ECHO works? A *copy* of the **5** is now inserted where the insert cursor was pointing (the replace cursor would have replaced existing characters, starting with the character under it).

A Command Line Summary

Review what you now know about the Command Line:

- You know how to type in a wide assortment of things—numbers and alphabetic characters, including lowercase letters, special symbols, and the NEWLINE character.

- You know how to use ◀, ▶, ▲, ▼, DEL, and ← to move around and edit the Command Line.

- You know that if you need even more tools—such as ◆SKIP, DEL◆, INS ☐ and ↑STK—you can also open the EDIT toolbox: ← EDIT.

But, _did you know?_... _When_ you're _not_ already working on something in the Command Line, ← EDIT lets you edit the object at Stack Level 1, by making a "working copy" of it for you on the Command Line!

Try It: Press CANCEL to clear the current Command Line. Then press ← EDIT.... The 43 has been _copied_ into the Command Line, ready to be modified. Press 2 ENTER. As usual, ENTER takes the object from the Command Line and put it onto the Stack. But in this case, it _replaces_ the original 43 with the new version of that object in the Command Line: 243.

Now try another: ← EDIT DEL · CANCEL. The CANCEL trashes only the edited version (.43) in the Command Line; it leaves the original 243 _intact_ at Level 1 of the Stack.

Simple Materials: Real Numbers

All right, it's time to look at what happens once you've succeeded in putting an object on the Stack—after you've finished typing on the Command Line and pressed (ENTER) to put the object at Level 1.

Real numbers are the most intuitive objects to start with, since you're somewhat familiar with them already: As you know, real numbers include the positive and negative integers $(1, 2, -3, -5$, etc.), the positive and negative rational numbers $(4.56, -2.3$, etc.), the positive and negative irrational numbers $(\sqrt{2}, \pi, e$, etc.), and zero (0).

Well, your 48 "sees" real numbers in much the same way that you do. They're easy to represent—just a set of digits—as in any calculator. But what about extremely large or small numbers—so awkward to deal with because their decimal representations use lots of placeholding zeroes (e.g. 00000001 and 1,000,000,000)?

That's why there's *scientific notation*.* Thus:

$$5,280 = 5.28 \times 10^3 \qquad 0.00023 = 2.3 \times 10^{-4} \qquad 1 = 1 \times 10^0$$

The *mantissa* shows the number's *precision*. It is then multiplied by a power of 10 (the "exponent"), to show the number's *magnitude*.

Actually, the 48 uses a slightly compacted version of this notation—to avoid the need for superscripts in its line-oriented display:

$$5,280 = \mathtt{5.28E3} \qquad 0.00023 = \mathtt{2.3E\text{-}4} \qquad 1 = \mathtt{1E0}$$

---

*Not that it's any more "scientific" than other notations, but science is one discipline where you commonly encounter very large or very small numbers. It could as easily have been called "national debt notation," for example.

Real Number Limitations on the 48

As you would expect, the 48 uses this scientific notation to achieve a huge range in real-number calculations. But it's still a finite machine with a few reasonable limitations that you need to understand.

12-Digit Accuracy: Some real numbers simply have infinite decimal representations. For example, $\frac{1}{3}$ is really 0.333.... But of course, it's impossible to use all of those 3's during arithmetic. Naturally, you round it, shortening it to a value that is both convenient and accurate enough for your purposes. Though the rounded number is *not* the same as the original, the difference is usually negligible in practice.

So, when dealing with infinite or extremely long decimal representations, the 48 rounds them, keeping a 12-digit mantissa of each number. The inaccuracy that results is *rounding error,* and—as you would expect—multiplying two rounded numbers will multiply this error.

So, how great an error is this?

Suppose you're the pilot of a plane flying from Los Angeles to New York. And it's a lovely day, and once airborne, your navigator lets it slip that he's been using his 48 to do fuel calculations—so his computations of miles per pound of fuel are accurate only to .000000000001 miles (uh-oh).... How big an error is this over 3,000 miles?

About *one two-hundredth of a millimeter.* If you'd flown clear to the *moon* and back, the error would be about 0.8 mm. And in a round trip to the sun, you'd be off by about a foot. Not a lot, really.

So the 48's 12-digit accuracy is slightly more than barely adequate.

Magnitude: Another limitation of the 48 is the *magnitude* of a real numbers (i.e., the value, not the number of digits) it can represent: You simply cannot expect it to represent arbitrarily large or small numbers. Everyone has a limit; you do—and so does your machine.

The largest real-number value representable on the 48 is a number called MAXR: 9.99999999999E499   (9.99999999999 × 10^{499})

And the smallest value, called MINR, is 1E-499   (1 × 10^{-499})

These numbers are fantastically large and small. It is difficult—if not truly impossible—to contemplate these quantities.*

---

*"It's a tough job—but someone's gotta do it:" Compare MAXR and MINR with some of the largest and smallest things in the known universe....

The effective radius of an electron is about 2.817938 × 10^{-15} m(eters)—or about 2.978626 × 10^{-31} light years (a light year is the distance that light travels through free space in one year's time). So the *volume* of an electron (assuming it's a sphere) is about 9.373093 × 10^{-44} cubic meters, or about 1.106972 × 10^{-91} cubic light years. Now, the radius of the sphere of the known universe is about 10^{10} light years—so its volume is about 10^{30} cubic light years. And so, if you were to pack the known universe absolutely solidly with electrons (no wasted space), you'd need about 10^{121} electrons.

Now that's a lot—more than anybody can really envision. But MAXR on the 48 is *so much larger* than *this*, that if you really had a collection of MAXR electrons, you'd have enough electrons to fill 10,000, 000,000,000,000,000,000,000,000,000,000,000,000,000,000,000,000,000,000,000,000,000,000 000,000,000,000,000,000,000,000,000,000,000,000,000,000,000,000,000,000,000,000,000,000 000,000,000,000,000,000,000,000,000,000,000,000,000,000,000,000,000,000,000,000,000,000 000,000,000,000,000,000,000,000,000,000,000,000,000,000,000,000,000,000,000,000,000,000 000,000,000,000,000,000,000,000,000,000,000,000,000,000,000,000,000,000,000,000,000,000 *known universes.*

On the small end of things, picture in your mind the colossal gob of electrons numbered above. Then picture yourself picking out just ten of those electrons. That ten—in relation to the whole—is the fraction you're talking about when you use the smallest 48 real value, MINR.

Suffice it to say that the magnitude limits of the 48 aren't all that restrictive.

Indeed, you may have heard of human cultures whose numbering systems went something like:

"1...2...3...more-than-3..."

...and that was all the higher they described numerical magnitude.

Well, so it is in every society. In this modern-day, technical world, for example, the numbering goes beyond 3, but at some point, it runs out of names and meanings too:

"...millions ... billions ... trillions ... quadrillions ..."

...and so on, up to about "nonillions"—about 10^{30}. But what do you call numbers on the order of 10^{100}, or 10^{400}?*

Truly, there is a limit to your practical needs to describe numbers. Yours may simply be a little higher than another's—but not by much.

---

*The authors recommend the term "several gadzillion."

Changing Signs and Entering Exponents

All right—enough worrying about the limitations of real numbers. It's time to see how they work as objects you manipulate on your workbench—the Stack. Try putting some real numbers on the bench-top....

Do This: Press CANCEL ← CLEAR MTH 5 2 8 0 ENTER 3 6 5 · 2 5 ENTER 6 · 0 2 2 α E 2 3 ENTER. You should see:

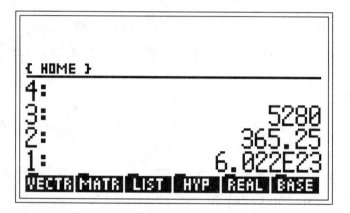

Notice that when you keyed in **6.022E23**, you used α E to key in the exponent—but you could have used EEX (Enter EXponent) instead.

For keying in exponents like this, EEX works much the same as α E except for one case: Press EEX now....

See what happens? If there's no mantissa already on the Command Line, EEX gives you one: 1.

(Press CANCEL now to clear the Command Line.)

Now, how about negative numbers? Try these...

Examples: Press $\boxed{1}$ $\boxed{\text{ENTER}}$ $\boxed{+/-}$ $\boxed{+/-}$....The $\boxed{+/-}$ key simply changes positive object values to negative—and vice versa.

Now put -1.3, 4.5×10^{-24}, -7.8×10^{3} and -9×10^{-54} onto the workbench. Press:

$\boxed{1}$ $\boxed{\cdot}$ $\boxed{3}$ $\boxed{+/-}$ $\boxed{\text{ENTER}}$

$\boxed{4}$ $\boxed{\cdot}$ $\boxed{5}$ $\boxed{\text{EEX}}$ $\boxed{2}$ $\boxed{4}$ $\boxed{+/-}$ $\boxed{\text{ENTER}}$

$\boxed{7}$ $\boxed{+/-}$ $\boxed{\cdot}$ $\boxed{8}$ $\boxed{\text{EEX}}$ $\boxed{3}$ $\boxed{\text{ENTER}}$

$\boxed{9}$ $\boxed{+/-}$ $\boxed{\text{EEX}}$ $\boxed{+/-}$ $\boxed{5}$ $\boxed{4}$ $\boxed{\text{ENTER}}$.

You'll see this:

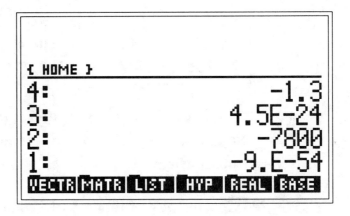

So there are two ways to get a negative number: You can put the positive number on the workbench in the usual way, then press $\boxed{+/-}$. Or, you can change the sign of either the mantissa or the exponent at any time while you're typing in that portion of the number.

Display Formats

You'll notice that the real numbers on the Stack have varying numbers of decimal places showing. What's going on?

Try This: Press ⬅(MODES) **FMT** (4) **FIX**. You should see:

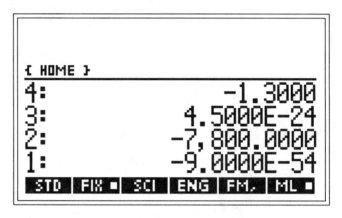

You just told the 48 to change the *format* of real numbers in the display. Their *values* haven't changed—just the way you see them.

(4) **FIX** tells the 48 to show a FIX'ed number of digits— four in this case—to the right of the decimal point.

Notice how the ☐ has appeared on the **FIX** mode key to tell you that FIX mode is currently set (recall page 19).

Now press (0) **FIX** ☐.... See? Now there are zero digits to the right of the decimal point. Again, the numbers haven't changed in value—only in appearance.

Do This: Press ⑴⑴ ▮SCI▮ .

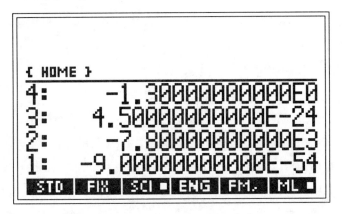

```
{ HOME }
4:          -1.30000000000E0
3:        4.50000000000E-24
2:          -7.80000000000E3
1:       -9.00000000000E-54
 STD | FIX | SCI □| ENG | FM. | ML □
```

Notice: In the previous examples some numbers were displayed in scientific notation even though the requested display mode was FIX. But that was only because it was impossible to display them any other way—using the 12 available digits. Any number greater than 999,999,999,999 or smaller than .000000000001 *must* be displayed in scientific notation, since its magnitude exceeds the ability of the display to show it as an explicit, one-part number.

But now, with SCI mode, you are *forcing* the display to use scientific notation for *every* number, regardless whether that number could otherwise be correctly represented in the display.

Finally—before going on—press ▮STD▮ . This is STandarD display format, where all significant digits are displayed and where scientific notation is used only when the number's value is outside of the display's magnitude limits.

Postfix Notation

"...Scientific notation, real-number representation limits, display formatting... when am I going to start *doing* things—like arithmetic—with real numbers?"

Right now:

Remember that what you're seeing in the display is quite literally a Stack of objects. Everything you've created so far has been "stacked up" on this "workbench."

Remember, too, that you put the latest additions on the *bottom* here; that's "upside-down" from your notion of a stack of lumber or pancakes. But it *is* a stack, nevertheless—because it's a *last-in-first-out* type of arrangement: the *last* thing you put onto the Stack is the *first* thing you take off.

With that in mind, here's the one simple rule to know as you begin working with the 48's Stack:

Whenever you use some *tool* to work on an *object*—say, to change the sign of a real number, for example—*the tool assumes that the object is already on the bench-top (i.e. on the Stack) when you start to use the tool.*

This means that you must first put onto the Stack any number(s) that you want to manipulate and *then* perform the operation. This way of doing things is called "postfix" (from *post-affix:* literally, "to add after") because the operation itself comes *after* the operands.

Real Number Tools

Try this *postfix* pattern of operation with some real-number tools.

Do It: Press ⑦ ⟨ENTER⟩. Now press ⟨1/x⟩.... What happens? The 7 is replaced by .142857142857, which is ⅟₇ (rounded to 12 digits). The ⟨1/x⟩ tool inverts the number in Stack Level 1.

Press ⟨1/x⟩ again. You get 7.00000000001   That's $\frac{1}{1/7}$.

Try another: Press ④ ⊡ ③ ⟨√x⟩....You get 2.07364413533—the square root of the 4.3 that was at Level 1. *But how did that 4.3 get to Level 1?* You never pressed ⟨ENTER⟩ to send it there from the Command Line—you just pressed ⟨√x⟩!

Answer: When you're working in the Command Line, most tools automatically put the contents of that Command Line onto the Stack (i.e. "press ⟨ENTER⟩" for you) before they start working—just to save you a step.

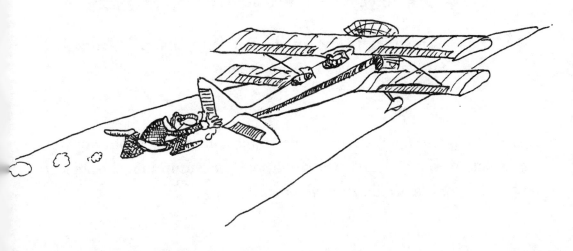

Notice: The *inverse* of a tool is often located on the same key as the tools itself. For example, press ⟵x^2 now.... You will get 4.29999999999, which is $\left(\sqrt{4.3}\right)^2$ to 12 digits.

But there are far more tools than keys, so—as usual—when you want more tools, look in a toolbox....

Like So: Press (MTH) to open the MaTH toolbox. From the menu that appears, you can see that this toolbox has six "drawers" in it. You can tell that they're drawers and not tools because they each have a "folder tab" on their top, left-hand corner.

Select the **REAL** drawer.... You now see six tools in this REAL menu, but remember that there may be more than these six tools in this drawer—and you can see more by pressing (NXT) or ⟵(PREV).

So "rummage" around in this toolbox now, until you find the **IP** (Integer Portion) tool. Try it—press **IP** ....

The result is 4—the Integer Portion of the 4.29999999999 that was at Level 1 of the Stack.

Again, the point is, whether you use tools from the keyboard or from some toolbox, they all make the same *postfix* assumption: the object to be "worked on" is *already on the Stack*.

Two-Number Tools

The tools you've seen so far have worked on one object on the Stack—at Level 1—the closest object to you. But many tools are designed to combine *two* objects to form another—as in "plain old arithmetic...."

Do Some: Add two real numbers on the Stack: Press ⬚1⬚ ⬚ENTER⬚ ⬚2⬚ ⬚+⬚. The result is no big surprise, right?

Try ⬚3⬚ ⬚ENTER⬚ ⬚4⬚ ⬚X⬚. Also no surprise.

Now, addition and multiplication are *commutative* operations (that is, $1 + 2 = 2 + 1$ and $3 \times 4 = 4 \times 3$). But that's not true for subtraction and division—so which number do you put onto the Stack first?

Just put the two numbers onto the bench-top in the order that you would say them. Thus $8 - 2$ would be ⬚8⬚ ⬚ENTER⬚ ⬚2⬚ ⬚−⬚; and $6 \div 4$ is ⬚6⬚ ⬚ENTER⬚ ⬚4⬚ ⬚÷⬚. Try those....

Notice also that several of the keyboard tools use x and y in their names. This is to help you remember where in the Stack the operand(s) should be to correctly use these tools:

The number at Level 1 is x; the number at Level 2 is y.

So, ⬚5⬚ ⬚ENTER⬚ ⬚3⬚ ⬚y^x⬚ calculates 5^3; and ⬚8⬚ ⬚1⬚ ⬚ENTER⬚ ⬚4⬚ ⬚→⬚ ⬚x√y⬚ finds $\sqrt[4]{81}$.

There are other one- and two-number math tools in the other MTH toolboxes, too. Check them out, if you want.

Stack Manipulations

So that's the basic idea: You put objects on your 48's postfix Stack workbench and then use tools on them.

Of course, you've seen this only with real numbers so far—and there are plenty of other objects and tools to learn. But first you ought to know how to organize, arrange and rearrange your workbench—the Stack. As you might expect, there are tools to help you do this....

The first and most basic of these is ←[CLEAR]. As its name implies, it clears the Stack, throwing away every object on it.

Do It Now: ←[CLEAR]

Another commonly used command is ←[DROP]. It throws away the object currently on Level 1 of the Stack, then drops all remaining objects down one level.

Try This: Press [1][ENTER][2][ENTER][3][ENTER]
                 ←[DROP]←[DROP]←[DROP].

Or This: [1][ENTER][2][ENTER][3][ENTER][◀][◀][◀].

As long as the Command Line is *not* active, [◀] is DROP (but of course, if you *are* typing in the Command Line, then [◀] is backspace).

Now, what if you want to duplicate the object at Level 1? (You'll want to do this a lot, as you'll soon see.)

Guess what? [ENTER] serves that purpose. Remember that when the Command Line is active, [ENTER] places its contents on the Stack. But when the Command Line is *not* active, [ENTER] makes a copy of the level 1 object and pushes it onto the Stack.

Example: Press [6] [ENTER] [ENTER] [ENTER]....

The first [ENTER] puts the 6 on the Stack at Level 1. The second [ENTER] copies this 6, pushing the original up a Level; you now have two 6's. The third [ENTER] again copies the bottom 6 and pushes the fresh copy onto Level 1, again pushing the existing objects up a Level; you now have three 6's. Press [←][CLEAR] now to clear them all.

The last of the common bench-top organizers is [←][SWAP]. It simply swaps Stack Levels 1 and 2, which is useful when working with order-sensitive tools such as subtraction and division. Similar to [←][DROP], when the Command Line is not active, you needn't press [←] to use [SWAP].

Try It: Press [1] [ENTER] [2] [ENTER] [3] [ENTER] [←][SWAP] (or just [SWAP]— that's the [▶] key). See? The 2 and 3 are swapped. Play around with this, and then press [←][CLEAR] to go on....

The Interactive Stack

The workbench can become pretty crowded with projects and raw materials in various stages of completion. Organizing, throwing away or bringing down selected items can be a real chore. But—how'd you guess?—there's a tool to help you.

Watch: First, put some "stuff" on the bench-top to play with. Press:
⟨←⟩⟨CLEAR⟩ ⟨1⟩ ⟨ENTER⟩ ⟨2⟩ ⟨ENTER⟩ ⟨3⟩ ⟨ENTER⟩ ⟨4⟩ ⟨ENTER⟩ ⟨5⟩ ⟨ENTER⟩ ⟨6⟩ ⟨ENTER⟩ ⟨7⟩ ⟨ENTER⟩ ⟨8⟩ ⟨ENTER⟩ ⟨9⟩ ⟨ENTER⟩ ⟨1⟩⟨0⟩ ⟨ENTER⟩

Now, press ⟨▲⟩ and see this:

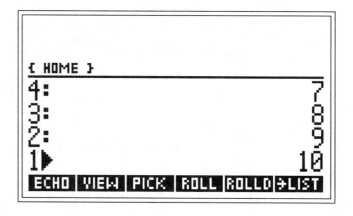

This is the *Interactive Stack*. It is designed to give you a quick and easy way to look at, edit and use an object at *any* Level in the Stack.

Remember the ↑STK tool in the EDIT toolbox (page 38)? Well, the Interactive Stack's arrow keys work in the same way: ⟨▲⟩ and ⟨▼⟩ move the pointer up and down the Stack. And ⟨→⟩⟨▲⟩ and ⟨→⟩⟨▼⟩ jump all the way to the extreme top and bottom of the Stack, respectively.

Do This: Move to Level 1 now if you're not there (i.e., press ⟨→⟩⟨▼⟩).

ECHO should look familiar, too. It works like EDIT's **ECHO** except that it *opens* the Command Line (because there isn't one already) and echoes into it the object at the pointer Level. Try it—press **ECHO**....

Nothing *seems* to happen, except for the changed menu, but the Command Line *is* open—with 10 in it. But before showing it to you, the machine is giving you a chance to move around the Stack and echo other Levels, too.

Press ⟨▲⟩⟨▲⟩ **ECHO** ⟨ENTER⟩. *Now* the Command Line appears—and it contains the 10 *and* the 8 that you've echoed from the Stack. And if you were to press ⟨ENTER⟩ now, those numbers would go onto the Stack—just as they would if you had *typed* this Command Line instead. But press ⟨CANCEL⟩ to discard them. Notice that you've left the Interactive Stack; press ⟨▲⟩ to reactivate it.

Notice also the next item in the Interactive Stack menu: **VIEW**. It works just like ⟨←⟩⟨EDIT⟩ except that it edits the *object being pointed-to*—creating a working copy on the Command Line so that ⟨ENTER⟩ and ⟨CANCEL⟩ can either accept or reject the changes you made.

Again, the idea of the Interactive Stack is to let you move around the Stack and work with any object as you normally do with the bottom-most object.

Continue across the Interactive Stack's menu items:

PICK makes a copy of the pointed-to object and pushes this copy onto the Stack at Level 1, moving everything else up a Level.

Try It Now: Make copies of Levels 3 and 11. Press: ⟶▽▲▲
PICK ⟶▲ **PICK** ⟶▽ and see:

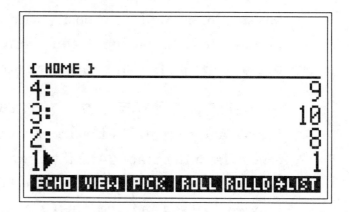

Then Notice: **ROLL** and **ROLLD** "roll" the contents of the Stack between Level 1 and the pointer's Level. **ROLL** rolls up; **ROLLD** rolls down.

Move the pointer to Level 4 (▲▲▲) and press **ROLL** several times to see the effect. Each time, the four numbers are "rolled up," with the Level-4 number coming down to replace the Level-1 number.

And **ROLLD** rolls the other direction. So roll Levels 1 through 4 around until you've had enough, then put them back in their original order: 9 10 8 1.

Now turn to the next page of the Interactive Stack menu (press [NXT]) to see more tools.... These tools use the Level number of the pointer as a kind of counter—telling the machine how many Levels to *duplicate*, *drop* or *keep*.

Examples: Move the pointer to Level 2 and press **DUPN**. You see:

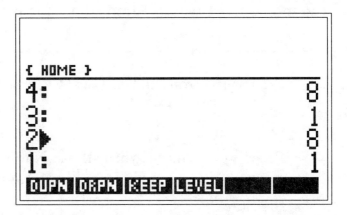

You now have two copies of the contents of Levels 1 and 2. The duplicate set was pushed onto the bottom of the Stack—bumping the originals up to Levels 3 and 4.

DRPN drops (discards) the pointed-to level *and everything below it*. Press **DRPN** now to drop levels 1 and 2. Conversely, **KEEP** *keeps* the pointed-to Level and everything below it—but discards everything above it. Press **KEEP** now.... See? Only Levels 1 and 2 remain.

LEVEL simply pushes the *Level number* of the pointer onto the Stack. Press **LEVEL** now, while pointing to Level 2, and watch as the 48 pushes a 2 onto the Stack.

Finally, there's one other Interactive Stack tool that's not in the toolbox (the menu)—because it's on the keyboard: ⬅

As you may remember from page 52, when there's no Command Line, ⬅ acts as a DROP (identical to ←)DROP)), which discards the Level-1 object.

Well, in the Interactive Stack, ⬅ drops the *pointed-to* object....

Prove It: Press ⬅ to drop the 1 at Level 2. Press ⬅ again to drop the 8.

Press ⬅ once more to drop the 2. Notice how the pointer won't ever go any higher than the highest filled Level of the Stack.

Notice also that dropping the last object on the Stack terminates Interactive Stack—you're back to the menu you were looking at before that—probably somewhere in the MaTH menu.

You can see that the 48 is designed to be as convenient as possible: Maybe you went into the Interactive Stack to do some vast (or half-vast) Stack manipulations, object building, copying—who knows? But the *reason* for it all might be that you need to use something in this MaTH menu on the resulting object(s). So the 48 remembers which menu you were in and treats the Interactive Stack excursion as just a temporary "side-trip"—a "time-out" for preparations.

Learning By Doing

By now, you're surely reeling with all the tools at your disposal—just to "mess around" in the Stack. Look how much you've seen:

- You know how to type on the Command Line, and how to use the α key (one α per character or α α to "lock" it on);

- You know how to use lowercase letters, NEWLINE and other special characters;

- You know how to edit the Command Line with, DEL, ◄ and the EDIT toolbox, which (among other things) lets you choose between the insert (♦) and the overwrite (▮) cursors and ECHO objects from the Stack into the Command Line

- You know various and sundry other things, too.

Of course, there's no way you're going to memorize all the various Stack and Command Line manipulation tools just through brief introductions like these—so don't panic if a lot of this has blurred together by now.

But *now is the time* to drive it home to yourself: The best way to become familiar with the tools and concepts presented in this chapter is to *use* them. So there's a quiz on the following pages—mainly real-number math and Stack problems. You may not be able to work every problem correctly the first time. If you get stuck, look at the answer! See how it's done. Then work the problem again until you understand the solution. After you've done all these problems, think up some of your own. Play with the Stack—get used to it. Master it.

Workbench Quiz

1. Find $\quad 1 + 2 + 3 + 4$

    Find $\quad 1 + 2 + 3 \times 4$ $\qquad$ Then find $\qquad (1 + 2 + 3) \times 4$

    Find $\quad 1 + 2 \div 3$ $\qquad$ Then find $\qquad (1 + 2) \div 3$

2. Find $\quad \dfrac{1}{2 + 3}$

3. Find $\quad \dfrac{2\ln(7)}{45}$

4. Find $\quad \dfrac{-12 + \sqrt{12^2 - 4(3)(-5)}}{2(3)}$

5. Find $\quad 173e^{\left[\frac{-16 + 43(.004)}{32 - 16.3}\right]}$

6. Find $\quad 1 + .5 + \dfrac{.5^2}{2!} + \dfrac{.5^3}{3!} + \dfrac{.5^4}{4!}$

7. Find both answers: $\quad \dfrac{16 \pm \sqrt{(-16)^2 - 4(20)(-48)}}{2(20)}$

8. Find $\sin 45°$, $\cos 134\,\text{grad}$, and $\arcsin 0.5$, in radians.

9. For $\theta = 75°$, show that: $\sin 3\theta = 2\sin\theta\cos^2\theta + \left(1 - 2\sin^2\theta\right)\sin\theta$

10. What are the differences in rounding error for $\sin \pi$ radians if you round π to 4 decimal places? 11 places? What if you *truncate* at 4 decimal places? 11 places?

11. With 26 refrigerator magnets, one of each letter in the alphabet, how many different six-letter "words" can you make? What if no two "words" may use the same six magnets?

12. By what percentage must you decrease $\dfrac{\sqrt{5}+1}{2}$ to get $\dfrac{\sqrt{5}-1}{2}$?

13. Put the numbers 12, 34, 56, 78, and 90 onto the Stack. Now reverse their order (without typing them in again).

14. Without typing any digits, form the least possible positive integer from the digits of the five numbers in the previous problem.

Workbench Solutions*

1. [1][ENTER][2][+][3][+][4][+]   <u>Answer:</u> 10
   [1][ENTER][2][+][3][ENTER][4][×][+]   <u>Answer:</u> 15
   [1][ENTER][2][+][3][+][4][×]   <u>Answer:</u> 24
   [1][ENTER][2][ENTER][3][÷][+]   <u>Answer:</u> 1.66666666667
   [1][ENTER][2][+][3][÷]   <u>Answer:</u> 1

   Remember: In the absence of parentheses, do multiplication before addition. When construing a written arithmetic problem to solve on the Stack, work from the highest operator priority to the lowest—and from the innermost parentheses outward.

2. [2][ENTER][3][+][1/x]   <u>Answer:</u> .2

3. [7][→][LN][2][×][4][5][÷]   <u>Answer:</u> 8.64848955138E-2

4. [1][2][←][x²][4][ENTER][3][×][5][+/−][×][−][√x][1][2][+/−][+]
   [2][ENTER][3][×][÷]   <u>Answer:</u> .38047614285

5. [4][3][ENTER][·][0][0][4][×][1][6][+/−][+][3][2][ENTER][1][6][·][3][−][÷]
   [←][eˣ][1][7][3][×]   <u>Answer:</u> 63.1263787068

*Keep in mind that there are many ways to solve arithmetic problems on the Stack. The solutions shown here are among the most straightforward and easiest to understand. But there are certainly other solutions—some of which use fewer keystrokes—so use whatever methods make sense to you. Unless otherwise noted, the answers assume STD display notation.

6. [1] [ENTER] [·] [5] [+] [·] [5] [←] [x²] [2] [MTH] [NXT] `PROB` `!` [÷] [+]
[·] [5] [ENTER] [3] [yˣ] [3] `!` [÷] [+]
[·] [5] [ENTER] [4] [yˣ] [4] `!` [÷] [+] Answer: 1.6484375

As you can see, the PROB toolbox in your MTH menu has the factorial function, to help you "crunch" this Taylor expansion by brute force; later you'll see another function to make this easier.

7. [1] [6] [ENTER] [2] [ENTER] [2] [0] [X] [÷]
[1] [6] [+/-] [←] [x²] [4] [ENTER] [2] [0] [X] [4] [8] [+/-] [X] [-] [√x] [2] [ENTER] [2] [0] [X] [÷]
[▲] [▲] [NXT] `DUPN` [CANCEL] [+]   Answer: 2
[◄] [-]   Answer: -1.2

Keep in mind your Interactive Stack.

8. [←] [MODES] `ANGL` `DEG` (if necessary) [4] [5] [SIN]
                        Answer: .707106781187
`GRAD` [1] [3] [4] [COS]   Answer: -.50904141575
`RAD` [·] [5] [←] [ASIN]   Answer: .523598775598

You've seen the MODES menu before. Here you use it to set the *angle mode*—degrees, radians or grads.

9. [←] [MODES] `ANGL` `DEG` [7] [5] [ENTER] [3] [X] [SIN] [7] [5] [SIN] [ENTER] [ENTER]
[←] [x²] [2] [X] [1] [-] [+/-] [X] [▶] [2] [X] [7] [5] [COS] [←] [x²] [X] [+]
Answers: -.707106781187   and   -.707106781181

That's close enough, allowing for rounding error (see prob. **10**).

10. π is 3.14159265358979323846…. But no machine represents it (or any irrational value) exactly; any numerical computation *must* approximate. As for all values, the 48 uses a 12-digit representation of π (11 decimal places), then *rounds* for best accuracy:

3.14159265358979323846…   ---->   **3.14159265359**

To *truncate* would decrease the accuracy:
3.14159265358979323846…   ---->   **3.14159265358**

The same argument is true at the fourth decimal place:
3.14159265358979323846…   ---->   **3.1416**
3.14159265358979323846…   ---->   **3.1415**

The sine function is sensitive* to such approximations of π: Since $\sin \pi \equiv 0$, any approximation greater than π gives a *negative* sine; any "under-approximation" gives a *positive* sine:

(←)(MODES) **ANGL** **RAD** (3)(·)(1)(4)(1)(5)(9)(2)(6)(5)(3)(5)(9)(ENTER)
(ENTER)(ENTER)(ENTER)(SIN)   Answer: **-2.06761537357E-13**
(◆)(EEX)(+/-)(1)(1)(-)(SIN)   Answer: **9.79323846264E-12**
(◆)(MTH) **REAL** (←)(PREV)(4) **RND** (SIN)
      Answer: **-7.3464102067E-6**
(◆)(4) **TRNC** (SIN)   Answer: **9.26535896607E-5**

The RND and TRNC functions round or truncate to the number of decimal places you specify (4 here). A *negative* specifier requests that many *significant digits* (rather than decimal places).

*This isn't true for all angles. For example, sin 1.5707963268 (sin " $\pi/2$ ") is **1.00000000000**—to 11 decimal places—but only because the rounding happens to works out, not because the 48 treats π somehow specially in its numeric calculations. It *never uses* π itself and can never give answers other than those produced by the digits it does use. This is true for any irrational number: Take $\sqrt{2}$ on the 48 and then square the 12-digit answer. You do *not* (and *should* not) get **2.00000000000** (do the arithmetic by hand, to prove this, if you wish: 1.41421356237 × 1.41421356237). Any calculator that gives you 2.00000000000 for that answer (or 0.00000000000 for sin 3.14159265359) is doing "funny math"—and you should feel free to be outraged.

11. This is a probability problem—go to the PROB tool box: `MTH` `NXT` `PROB`. The question is, how many *permutations* (the order matters) can you make of 26 objects, taking 6 at a time?

`2` `6` `ENTER` `6` `PERM`   Answer: `165765600`

If the order doesn't matter, then it's *combinations* of 26, taking 6 at a time: `2` `6` `ENTER` `6` `COMB`   Answer: `230230`

12. `5` `√x` `1` `+` `2` `÷`   (Result: `1.61803398875`)
`5` `√x` `1` `-` `2` `÷`   (Result: `.61803398875`)

Now, the percentage calculations are kept in the REAL toolbox, so `MTH` `REAL` `%CH`   Answer: `-61.803398875`

That's a 61.80...% decrease (it's a *negative* change).

13. Press `1` `2` `ENTER` `3` `4` `ENTER` `5` `6` `ENTER` `7` `8` `ENTER` `9` `0` `ENTER`.
Of course, there are many solutions to the reversal problem. here's one with the Interactive Stack: `▲` `▲` `ROLL` `▲` `ROLL` `▲` `ROLL` `▲` `ROLL` `ENTER`.

14. The key here is to use the Interactive Stack to ECHO items from the Stack onto your Command Line: `▲` `ECHO` `▲` `ECHO` `▲` `ECHO` `▲` `ECHO` `▲` `ECHO` `ENTER`. That sends you to the Command Line, where all you need to do is delete the space delimiters*: `←` `EDIT` `←` `←SKIP` `←` `←SKIP` `←` `←SKIP` `←` `←SKIP` `←` `ENTER`.

---

*Technically, the smallest positive integer possible is `0123456789`, which, when `ENTER`'ed, would be `123456789`, so you could argue that it's "legal" to delete the `0` character here too. ("OK, *fine*.")

3 OBJECTS: YOUR RAW MATERIALS

The Fundamental Idea

This chapter is an introduction to the basic raw materials—"objects"—in your 48 workshop. You may not use all of these objects, but read this chapter completely, anyway—so that at least you'll know what options you have for solving problems. Many solutions on the 48 use more than one type of object, so take the time now to understand the basics of each type—even if you don't see what good it is right away.

Besides, this will give you a better understanding of the 48's way of doing things—its Fundamental Idea: *You can generalize the problem-solving process.* Once you know the keystrokes and strategies for problem-solving with one type of object, you can use other objects similarly —without learning entire new sets of commands and rules.

Real Numbers

You've already seen real numbers in action on the 48—to show you how postfix arithmetic works on the Stack. The only point to reiterate here is this:

Just as you combine real numbers on the Stack via real-number math functions, so you combine other objects via math functions, often using the same function keys (e.g. ⊞ ⊟ ⊠ ⊟, *etc.).*

So now it's time to look at how these other object types work. Of course, to use them, you must know how to build and recognize them, too....

Units

In a sense, real numbers aren't so real. When you add 1 to 2, what does that mean? 1 *what?* 2 *whats?* 3 *whats?*

In the real *world,* you generally talk about real numbers as indicating quantities of *something.* When you drive 100 miles one day and 75 the next, you speak of distances; the basic unit of measure is the mile. When you fill your gasoline tank by adding 7.4 gallons to your 15 gallon tank, you're talking about volume, with a basic unit of a gallon.

The point is, you wouldn't need to specify such units if everybody measured things the same way; if that were the case, you *could* simply use real numbers. But it's not. You can add 1 foot to 1 yard and get 4 feet or 1.3333 yards. And just how many teaspoons of liquid are there in a liter? And how many square feet in an acre? Sometimes, doing the unit conversions and checking your units for consistency are the most difficult parts of doing a calculation.

How does the 48 represent them?

The 48 allows you to *associate* units with real numbers—much as you do now. When you associate values and units on paper, you write the unit after the value: 14 ft   26.3 in   142 acre

The 48 does it very similarly, simply using an underscore (_) to link the real number with its unit:

```
14_ft          26.3_in          142_acre
```

How do you build a unit object?

The easiest way to create a unit object is to use the UNITS toolbox....

Do This: Press ⬅[CLEAR], then open the UNITS toolbox.

Like So: Press ➡[UNITS].... Notice that each of the resulting menu items is a drawer with an "tab"—telling you that each leads to yet another menu—a sub-menu with more selections (use [NXT] to see all 16 submenus available): LENGth, AREA, VOLume, TIME, SPEED, MASS, FORCE, ENeRGy, POWeR, PRESSure, TEMPerature, ELECtricity ANGLe, LIGHT, RADiation and VISCosity.

On the first page of the menu, select the LENGth sub-menu: **LENG**. Looking through this menu, you'll find 22 different units of length.

To build a unit object, simply key in the real number value and press the corresponding unit key. For example, to build the unit object 14_ft, press [1][4] **FT** (do this now)....* By pressing the **FT** key, you created a single unit, 1_ft, and then *multiplied* this by the real number, 14, to form the unit object, 14_ft.

That's true in general: Pressing any unit key forms a value of 1 of that unit, then *multiplies* that by the object already at Level 1 of the Stack.

---

*The menu keys show all letters in upper case, but the unit name itself often uses lower case.

How do you use a unit object?

The beauty of unit objects is that *you use them just as you would real numbers—and the 48 will keep track of the units automatically.*

Example: Calculate how many feet of 10-inch-wide lumber planks you'll need to build a 7-level (backless) shelf unit that is 2 meters tall, 1 yard wide and 10 inches deep.

Solution: You need seven 1-yard pieces and two 2-meter pieces, each 10 inches wide. So press: ⏎[CLEAR] [1] **YD** [7][×] [2] **M** [2][×][+] ⏎ **FT**. <u>Answer*</u>: 34.12_ft

---

Things to notice:

- 1_yd x 7 = 7_yd. And 2 x 2_m = 4_m.
  Multiplying a unit object by a real number (scalar) gives you another unit object with the same units.

- 7_yd + 4_m = 10.40_m.
  Adding (or subtracting) two compatible unit objects gives you an object with units the same as that of the previous *Level-1* object.

- To convert a unit object to other compatible units, simply press ⏎ before pressing the desired unit's key. Any of the LENGth units are compatible with each other; any of the AREA units are compatible with one another, etc.

*Until further notice, all answers will assume a display mode of FIX 2 (so press ⏎[MODES] **FMT** [2] **FIX**, then return to your previous menu (UNITS LENGth) with a handy shortcut key, →[MENU]).

Now: You've just calculated the length of 10-inch planking you'll need. How many square feet of lumber is this?

Easy: Simply multiply this length by 10 inches: [1][0] ⬛ IN ⬛ [×].
Result: **341.23_ft*in**   *Notice* that the units of a product ([×] or [÷]) is *not* forced into the units of either of the previous values. Instead it forms a *combination* of those previous units. This is different than with a sum ([+] or [−]).

So you now have a correct area—but in rather uninformative "mixed" units—**ft*in**. To convert it to something more meaningful, simply move to the AREA menu ([→][UNITS] ⬛ AREA ⬛), and convert it to square feet: [←] ⬛ FT^2 ⬛.
Answer: **28.44_ft^2**

Notice that the 48 uses ^ to indicate raising to a power. That is, **ft^2** represents ft².

Question: What if you ask the 48 to add *incompatible units*?

Try It: Move back to the LENGth menu (press [→][UNITS] ⬛ LENG ⬛) and try to add **1_ft** to the square feet from the above answer (press [1] ⬛ FT ⬛ [+])…. No go, right? The 48 says:

$$+ \text{ Error:}$$
$$\text{Inconsistent Units}$$

The 48 saves you from these common—but deadly—unit errors.

Press CANCEL to clear that error message, and practice some more....

Problem: It's roughly 700 km by road from Calgary to Saskatoon, and you've just filled up in Calgary with 50 liters of fuel. You know that your car gets about 35 miles per U.S. gallon in the kind of driving conditions you expect. Can you make it all the way to Saskatoon without refueling?

Solution: As with most problems, there are several ways to do this. One way is to convert your car's mpg rating into kilometers/liter: At the LENGth menu, press NXT 3 5 MI →UNITS VOL NXT → GAL (the → key is other variation available on each unit key: just as the unshifted GAL key *multiplies* 1_gal by the Level-1 object, so → GAL *divides*).

There's your known mpg. Now build your desired units: 1 → L , then →MENU 0 KM ×....

Why *zero* km∕l? Because then you can convert your answer to km∕l simply by *adding* this zero harmlessly to your 35_mi∕gal (recall what addition does with units)! Do it: + Result: 14.88_km∕l

This is your car's fuel usage rate in local units. Now, to see your car's probable range, just multiply your rate by your fuel supply: →UNITS VOL NXT 5 0 L ×.... Result: 744.00_km

---

Yep—barring unforeseen problems—you should make it to Saskatoon.

③ *Objects: Your Raw Materials*

That's one way to attack this kind of units conversion problem—using the 48's ability to convert between compatible units during addition. But there's a more direct way....

Recalculate: When you reached Saskatoon and refueled, your 50-liter tank took 48.4 liters, and your trip-meter odometer showed 712.8 km. What was your actual mileage (miles per gallon) for the trip?

Solution: First, find your fuel usage in km∕l: ⟵CLEAR ⟶UNITS
LENG NXT 7 1 2 · 8 KM ⟶UNITS VOL
NXT 4 8 · 4 L ÷.... Result: 14.73_km∕l

Now build your desired units:
1 ⟶ GAL ⟶MENU MI.

Now here's the point where you can do things differently: Press ⟵UNITS (the *other* shift key).... This small menu has units *commands* on them—specific things you can do with unit objects.

That first item is the one you'll probably use the most: CONVert simply converts the object in Stack Level 2 to the *units* of the object in Level 1 (the *number* in Level 1 doesn't matter). Try it now—press CONV.... Result: 34.64_mi∕gal

---

So just remember that you can convert between units either through addition/subtraction or with the CONVert command (you'll explore the other items on the ⟵UNITS menu later).

Lists

Before you go on to explore the other object types available to you in the 48, consider this: A unit object is an *ordered collection* of two simpler "things"—a real number and a unit, in that order. The new object arises from this specifically ordered collection of otherwise distinct parts. This is a general pattern within the 48: More sophisticated "things" are often created from *collections* of simpler "things."

So what makes a collection an object? Simply gathering together an ordered collection of "things" doesn't mean anything by itself. 14_ft is an ordered collection of two "things"—but it means nothing *until* those numerals, underscore and letters are given *rules* governing their significance and use: "The numerals stand for a real number and may be mathematically treated as such; the underscore links the number with an associated (multiplied) unit."

The point is, only with such specific governing rules for manipulating and interpreting a collection does it become a distinct form—an *object*. Each object *type* is distinguished by a different set of these rules.

So what's a list?

A list is simply the object type with the most general (*least restrictive*) rules for manipulating and interpreting its collection of elements: It's just an ordered collection of objects of any type, listed together in a sequence. That's why it's called simply a *list*: there's no more specific mathematical or physical interpretation of it.

How does the 48 represent a list?

The telltale characteristic of a list is its enclosing set of { }. Here are examples of lists:

$$\{ 1\ 2\ 3\ 4\ 5\ 6\ 7\ \texttt{"Hi there"}\ 14\_feet\ \}$$

$$\{ \texttt{"Yo, dude!"}\ (3,4)\ \{ 1\ 2\ \}\ 98.6\_F\ \}$$

$$\{ [1\ 2\ ]\ (5,\angle 53.1)\ \{ \}\ \}$$

A list can contain any number of any type of object* in any mixture—including other lists—or even no objects at all.

*Some of the object types in these sample lists may be new to you yet. Don't sweat their details—just realize that they, too, may be elements of lists.

How do you build a list?

There are several ways to put a list onto your Stack workbench. Naturally, you can type it in directly from the Command Line....

Do This: Press ⟵[CLEAR] ⟵[{}] [1] [SPC] [2] [ENTER]....
                  You've just built the list **{ 1.00 2.00 }**

Easy, right? And did you notice the **PRG** sign in the Status Area while you were keying in the list? (Do the above exercise again, if you wish). This mode activates when you start the list, so that keystrokes that would normally execute immediately will instead just *record* their names as items in your list.

So use the ⟵[{}] key to start a list. Then you can key in any objects— even executable commands—as elements in that list.

Now, what about making lists from objects already on the Stack?

To start with, consider this: What happens when you add different (but compatible) *unit objects* on the Stack? The result takes the units of the previous Level-1 object, right? All right, then what do you think might happen when you try to add different object *types* together?

Find Out: Enter the objects 5 and 14_feet (press ←[CLEAR] 5 [ENTER] →[UNITS] **LENG** 1 4 **FT**), and then add them together ([+])....No can do, right? Nor does the order matter: Try the above addition again, reversing the order of the two objects. ...Nope. But you knew this from page 71, right?

Ah, but what if at least one of the objects is a *list*? Press [CANCEL] ←[{ }] 5 [ENTER].... Underline: Result: { 5.00 }

Now, try adding another object type to it. Press 2 [+]....

How about *that*? Make a copy ([ENTER]), and then try another object type: 1 4 **FT** [+]....

And what about adding *another list*? Press [+]....

Notice how the order matters: Try 1 [ENTER] [SWAP] [+]....

Moral of the story: *You can add unlike object types if at least one of them is a list.* If the non-list object is in Level 2, it will be appended to the *front* of the list; if at Level 1, it goes onto the *end* of the list.

The other question: How do create a list out of existing Stack objects where *none* of them are necessarily lists?

Try This: ⟵CLEAR 1 ENTER 2 ENTER 3 ENTER PRG **LIST** 3 **→LIST**
Result: { 1.00 2.00 3.00 }

You can put any number of Stack objects into a list simply by specifying that number and invoking **→LIST**.

Try another: ⟶UNITS **LENG** 1 4 **FT** 5 ENTER
⟵{} ENTER PRG **LIST** 4 **→LIST**   Result:
{ { 1.00 2.00 3.00 } 14_ft 5.00 { } }

Notice the order of list formation: First onto the Stack goes first into the list.

Notice also the list "length specifier"—the number that goes onto the Stack last, before you invoke **→LIST**. This is the *argument* of the **→LIST** command. With its postfix notation, the 48 assumes that all information necessary for the execution of any command is already on the Stack* when you invoke a command name; it won't stop and prompt you for anything more once you invoke the command.

You've already seen at least one argument in action: remember how you set the display to FIX 2 decimal places (page 70)? *First* you entered the 2—your argument—*then* you selected the command (**FIX**).

---

*or in the Command Line—remember that most executable commands come with a "built-in ENTER" that effectively puts the current Command Line on the Stack before proceeding.

One other key point about arguments on the Stack: The 48 reads each argument *and then discards* ((DROP)s) *it before proceeding with a command.* It never includes the argument(s) as part of the Stack when actually carrying out the command's actions. This is why, for example, you got { 1.00 2.00 3.00 } instead of { 2.00 3.00 3.00 } in the first exercise on the opposite page: the bottommost 3.00 was the *argument* of ▸LIST and was therefore read and dropped before ▸LIST was actually performed.*

So that's how to *build* a list from objects on the Stack. Now, can you take it apart again?

No Sweat: Press OBJ▸....   See what happens?

OBJ▸ is the 48's General Purpose Object Decomposer. That is, it breaks down virtually any compound object into its list of components, stacking up these components in order in the Stack. And for objects such as lists—that don't necessarily have a fixed number of components OBJ▸ also leaves the element count at Level 1—so that you can *re*-compose with a single command (▸LIST, in this case—try it)!

---

*To practice more with arguments, you might want to try some of the commands in the STACK toolbox ((←)(STACK)). This Course covered some of the basics of Stack manipulations in Chapter 2, mainly with the Interactive Stack. But if you stop and think about it for a moment, you'll realize that the pointer you moved around in the Interactive Stack is just a visual way of providing the 48 with an argument for those Stack commands that require it. When you're *not* in the interactive Stack, you can still use all those same Stack manipulation functions, but you must *key in* the necessary argument—just as you did here with ▸LIST.

Complex Numbers

Time to move on now, to learn about the next object type.

Mathematically, a *complex number* is a vector in the complex plane, an ordered pair of numbers representing the vector's coordinates. The coordinates are usually expressed in either rectangular form (*a+bi*) or in polar form (Z∡θ).

How does the 48 represent a complex number?

On the 48, a complex number is also an ordered pair of (i.e. a *list* of two) real numbers, which are *vector coordinates* expressed in either rectangular form (3.00, 4.00) or polar form (5.00, ∡53.13). The pair is surrounded by parentheses and separated by , and possibly ∡. Of course, you can use this pair to represent anything you want, but mathematically it is a complex number—to be added, multiplied, etc.

Try One: ⮐CLEAR ⮐() 3 SPC 4 ENTER. Result: (3.00, 4.00) This is the complex number 3+4*i*. Now press ENTER ENTER ENTER to make some copies, then +.... Complex addition is as easy as real addition. Press ×.... Also easy, no? Now DROP that result (leaving the last (3.00, 4.00) at Stack Level 1).

Question: When does the 48 display a complex number in rectangular form, and when in polar form?

Answer: It depends on the current *vector display mode.* Go to the MODES ANGL menu (press ⭠〔MODES〕 **ANGL**) and find the items **RECT▯**, **CYLIN** and **SPHER** (the ▯ means that RECTangular mode is now set): **RECT▯** displays complex numbers in *rectangular* mode; **CYLI▯** and **SPHE▯** display them in cylindrical and polar modes, respectively.

Try changing the mode and watch the complex number at Level 1 change its format (notice the annunciators in the Status Area, too). But keep in mind that the number retains its same (rectangular) complex value (3+4*i*); only its display *formatting* is being altered—for your eyes. This is true in general: Once you've keyed in a complex number, the machine "remembers" it internally in rectangular form, but it presents the number to you according to the current mode settings.

Question: How does the 48 know when to represent a complex number's vector *angle* in degrees, radians or grads?

Answer: It judges by the current *angular mode.* You can switch this mode—and thus the *polar* formats of the number— by pressing **RAD** or **GRAD** (try these now, but leave things in **DEG ▯** and **RECT▯** modes when you finish).

How do you build a complex number?

You have several ways to put a complex number onto the work bench—and you've already seen the most rudimentary way to do it.

Again: Type it in directly from the Command Line: Press ⏎[(][)][1] [SPC][2][ENTER]. This gives (1.00, 2.00), a complex number _in rectangular form._ (You could use either ⏎['] or [SPC]; both act as _delimiters_ to separate the parts of the number.)

Now change the mode to polar form (press ➡[POLAR]—a handy keyboard modes toggle). Of course, you won't get (1.00, ∡2.00), which is (1.00∠2.00°). Rather, you get the polar _representation_ of 1+2i—about (2.24∠63.43°). Remember, you don't change the existing vector _value_ by changing its _displayed format._

To actually key in a complex number _value_ in polar form, you must precede the second value with a ∡—because using a , or a [SPC] always means rectangular complex input to the 48. Try it: ⏎[(][)][1]➡[∡][2][ENTER]. _Now_ the 48 will take the second value to be an angle—in the current angle mode. _This_ is the value (1.00∠2.00°)—or about 1.00+.03i, as you can verify now by returning to rectangular mode (➡[POLAR]).

So that's the basic idea when _keying in_ complex-numbers—either in rectangular or polar format. But to build complex numbers from other values _already on the Stack,_ the 48 has some tools to help you....

Example: Put the numbers 5 and 10 on the Stack (⑤ ENTER ① ⓪ ENTER). Now use these two real numbers to form the rectangular complex number (5.00, 10.00).

Like This: Press MTH NXT, then select the `CMPL` toolbox. This is a menu of operations you can perform on complex numbers. Here you'll find `R→C` ("Real to Complex"). Try it now.... As you see, `R→C` takes two real numbers from the Stack, using the Level-2 number as the real portion and Level 1 as the imaginary portion of the new complex number.

And the `C→R` ("Complex to Real") goes the other way—taking apart the complex number and leaving two real numbers on the Stack. Try it now: `C→R`

The 48 is full of tools like these—designed to build or take apart a given type of object. And remember that there's one very "smart" operation that can dismantle virtually *any* object into its components....

Watch: Press `R→C` to rebuild (5.00, 10.00). Then PRG `LIST` `OBJ→`. Same effect as `C→R`, right? So here's a reminder: `OBJ→` is the *general-purpose object decomposition* tool.

But you can also extract the two parts of a complex number *mathematically*—with some specialized tools in the CMPL tool collection....

Challenge: Extract the two components of (3.00, 4.00)—both in rectangular and polar forms.

Solution: Key in the number (←()3 SPC 4) and make four copies of it (ENTER ENTER ENTER ENTER). Then press the MTH key and NXT **CMPL**. Here are some commands made to order "for all your extraction needs:"

RE extracts the REal portion: 3.00 (DROP that);

IM extracts the IMaginary portion: 4.00 (DROP it);

ABS extracts the ABSolute value of the complex number, which is simply the magnitude of its *polar* representation: 5.00 (now DROP that);

ARG extracts the angle (in the current angle mode) of the complex value in its polar form: 53.13

Complex Number Math

Complex numbers have mathematical properties similar to those of real numbers, so many of the 48's real-number operations also work for complex numbers. You've already seen complex arithmetic, but trigonometric and logarithmic functions work, too. And remember that you can use mixtures of complex and real numbers in complex math.

So practice some more now. As you do these, concentrate on your number entry format—and the 48's interpretation of it. Which *vector display mode* and which *angle display mode* is it using?

Challenge: Find $\dfrac{2}{3+i}$ and $\dfrac{3+i}{2}$ in rectangular format.

Solution: [2] [ENTER] [◁] [()] [3] [SPC] [1] [÷] .... <u>Result:</u> (0.60, -0.20)
[1/x] .... <u>Result:</u> (1.50, 0.50)

The 48 converts the real number 2.00 into the complex number (2.00, 0.00) before doing the division. Then just invert the first answer to get the second.

Another: Find $\ln(5\angle 1.618)$, in polar format.

Solution: Change the angle and vector modes: [◁] [RAD] [▷] [POLAR].
Then: [◁] [()] [5] [▷] [∠] [1] [·] [6] [1] [8] [▷] [LN] ....
<u>Result:</u> (2.28, ∠0.79)

Another: Find $\sin\sqrt{7+10i}$ rad in rectangular format.

Solution: [▷] [POLAR] (back to rectangular mode), then [◁] [()] [7] [SPC] [1] [0]. Now take the square root ([√x]), then the sine ([SIN]).
<u>Result:</u> (0.11, -2.41)

Another: Find $\dfrac{\ln 2 + i\sqrt{2}}{\sin 45° \times (1 + i\sqrt{3})}$ in rectangular format.

Solution: [2] [▷] [LN] [2] [+/-] [√x] [+]
[◁] [RAD] [4] [5] [SIN] [1] [ENTER] [3] [+/-] [√x] [+] [×] [÷] ....
<u>Result:</u> (1.11, 0.08)

Vectors

A complex number is one special kind of vector. But in general, a vector is an ordered list of numbers—usually representing dimensions (directions) in some physical sense. The typical vectors you use most often are therefore two-and three-dimensional ("2D" and "3D") quantities:

2D	**3D**

2D

rectangular notation

$$x\mathbf{i}+y\mathbf{j} \quad \text{or} \quad (x,y)$$

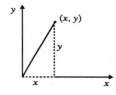

polar notation

$$(r,\theta)$$

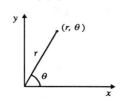

3D

rectangular notation

$$x\mathbf{i}+y\mathbf{j}+z\mathbf{k} \quad \text{or} \quad (x,y,z)$$

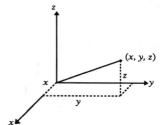

cylindrical notation

$$(r,\theta,z)$$

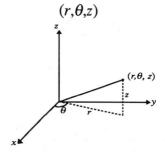

spherical notation

$$(\rho,\theta,\phi)$$

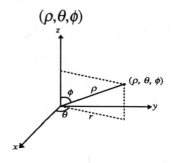

Vectors are more generally defined mathematically as *single-column matrices**—often encountered, for example, in linear systems:

$$\begin{bmatrix} a_{11} & a_{12} & a_{13} & a_{14} \\ a_{21} & a_{22} & a_{23} & a_{24} \\ a_{31} & a_{32} & a_{33} & a_{34} \\ a_{41} & a_{42} & a_{43} & a_{44} \end{bmatrix} \begin{bmatrix} x_1 \\ x_2 \\ x_3 \\ x_4 \end{bmatrix} = \begin{bmatrix} b_1 \\ b_2 \\ b_3 \\ b_4 \end{bmatrix}$$

In this capacity, of course, vectors are not limited to everyday physical interpretations; they may be *n*-dimensional ("*n*-**D**"). And their format is then only rectangular notation: $(a,b,c,d,e...)$

How does the 48 represent vectors?

Though you can use vector objects to represent anything you want, the 48 can also treat them as mathematical vectors. But since ( ) are used for complex numbers, vectors are bracketed within [ ]. *Notice* that a vector's elements may be real *or* complex—but not both:

2D	3D
[1 2]	[1 -2 3]
[3 ∡-30]	[6 ∡45 -19]
	[93 ∡121 ∡23.5]

n-**D**

[(1,2) (-1,4)]

[(5,∡37) (13.5,∡-155.9) (0,∡0)]

[2 34 19 -44 64 110 -25 37.5 9.09]

*The 48's display represents vectors *horizontally;* nevertheless, the machine uses them mathematically as *vertical* (single-*column*) matrices. Don't let the visual difference throw you.

How do you build a vector?

As usual, the most straightforward way to build a vector is to type it in directly from the Command Line. Try a few examples (these assume that your vector display and angle modes are as you left them in the last problem—rectangular and degrees, respectively):

Examples: Press ⬅[CLEAR], then ⬅[[ ]][1][SPC][2][SPC][3][SPC][4][ENTER].
Here's what you get: [1.00 2.00 3.00 4.00]

Press ⬅[[ ]][1]➡[∠][2][ENTER].... You get:
[1.00 0.03]
Of course, to see this in the polar form you had intended, just press ➡[POLAR].... [1.00 ∠2.00]

Press ⬅[[ ]][1][1]➡[∠][1][·][9][+/−][SPC][7][ENTER].... You get:
[11.00 ∠-1.90 7.00]
To see this in rectangular form, just press ➡[POLAR]....
[10.99 -0.36 7.00]

As you can see, the rules for separating components in vectors are the same as for complex numbers: You separate rectangular components with [SPC] (or **,**); you precede angular components with ∠. And keep in mind that the ∠ is meaningful only in the second and third components of **2D** and **3D** vectors. You won't be allowed to key it in anywhere else; and any vector larger than **3D** doesn't change from rectangular format when you change the vector display modes, anyway.

Speaking of vector display modes,...

Do This: Press (MTH) █████ (NXT).... Did you know those mode keys were available here—as well as in the MODES menu? As you see, HP has put some often-used commands in several places, so you needn't jump around as much to use them.

Something else to notice: At the moment, when you press →(POLAR) on the keyboard, it alternates (toggles) between rectangular and *cylindrical* (R∠Z) modes. But if you press █████, then →(POLAR) will toggle between rectangular and *spherical* (R∠∠) modes... (try it—and then leave the mode at rectangular and the toggle to cylindrical).

Now This: Press (NXT) to move to the first page of the VECTR menu. Now put two values on the Stack, (1)(2)(ENTER)(1)(5)(ENTER), and press ████ *to build a 2D vector from these values.* Easy, no? And the "loading" order of the vector's components is like those of complex numbers and lists: The higher in the Stack, the farther forward in the object.

Try a **3D** case: (2)(9)(ENTER)(4)(5)(ENTER)(1)(1) ████. Voilá. And ████ and ████ are *sensitive to the vector display mode.* To see this, press →(POLAR) to change to polar/cylindrical mode, then repeat the above keystrokes.... See the difference? The resulting vectors took the corresponding values to be angular. This is how to key in angular components without using the →(∠) key.

What goes up must come down: How do you tear apart vectors?

Easy: Just press ▐▜▟▐ —try it.... Thus, with either ▐÷V2▐ or ▐÷V3▐ and ▐▜▟▐ , you can go back and forth between the vector itself and its Stack of individual components.

Question: The commands in the VECTR menu are all good and fine for **2D** and **3D** vectors, but what about an *n*-**D** vector— of any arbitrary size? How do you build that?

Answer: Use an *argument*, just as for a list of arbitrary size. Go to the general *object-building* menu: (PRG) ▐TYPE▐ .

Now key in your *n*-**D** vector's values: [1](ENTER)[4](ENTER) [9](ENTER)[1][6](ENTER)[2][5](ENTER). Now press [5] ▐÷ARR▐ ....

Result: [1.00 4.00 9.00 16.00 25.00]

Your vector-size argument (5.00 here) is just like the list-length argument you use to build a list—except that you use ▐÷ARR▐ , instead of ▐÷LIST▐ , to do the building.*

---

*There's no command called ▐÷VEC▐ ; you use ▐÷ARR▐ because an *n*-**D** vector is actually a one-column *array* (matrix)—and the 48 treats it as such, mathematically. In fact, to break down an *n*-**D** vector into its components once again, you use ▐OBJ÷▐ (the All-Purpose, Whole-wheat, Recyclable, Bio-degradable, Universal Decomposer Tool), and it leaves the vector length argument as a *list* (the argument form used by arrays), rather than the *real number* argument you used to build the vector.

Vector Math

Now that you know how to build them and tear them apart, there's not much more to say about vectors in the 48 except "use them!"

Find: $\left| (3 + 4i, 7 + 11i) \right|$

Press: (in rectangular mode—[→][POLAR], if necessary), then [←][[ ]]
[←][( )][3][SPC][4][▶][←][( )][7][SPC][1][1][ENTER][MTH] **VECTR** **ABS**.
Result: **13.96**   A vector may be complex-valued, but ABS finds its *magnitude* ("length")—always a real value.

Find: $10(-1,-2,-3) + \dfrac{(4,5,6)}{2}$

Press: [1][0][ENTER][1][ENTER][2][ENTER][3] **→V3** [+/−][×][4][ENTER][5][ENTER]
[6] **→V3** [2][÷][+] Result: **[-8.00 -17.50 -27.00]**
You can *add* vectors of the same dimensions; and you can *multiply* any vector by any scalar (including **−1**, via [+/−]).

Find: $(1,2) \cdot (3,4)$ and $(3, \angle 45°, 10) \times (9, \angle 60°, 2)$

Press: [1][ENTER][2] **→V2** [3][ENTER][4] **→V2**
DOT   Result: **11.00**
The dot product of two same-dimension vectors is a scalar.

Then: [→][POLAR][3][ENTER][4][5][ENTER][1][0] **→V3** [9][ENTER][6][0]
[ENTER][2] **→V3** **CROSS**
Result: **[84.22 ∠151.06 6.99]**
The cross product of two **3D** vectors is another **3D** vector. And notice how easy it is to key in these cylindrical formats.

Arrays

In the most general sense, arrays are simply tables of "things" (dots, sticks, numbers—anything), arranged in rectangular formations of rows and columns:

$$
\begin{array}{cccc}
\bullet & \bullet & \bullet & \bullet \\
\bullet & \bullet & \bullet & \bullet \\
\bullet & \bullet & \bullet & \bullet \\
\bullet & \bullet & \bullet & \bullet
\end{array}
\qquad
\begin{array}{cc}
\nabla & \nabla \\
\nabla & \nabla \\
\nabla & \nabla
\end{array}
\qquad
\begin{array}{cc}
a_{11} & a_{12} \\
a_{21} & a_{22}
\end{array}
$$

$$
\begin{array}{ccccc}
\perp & \perp & \perp & \perp & \perp \\
\perp & \perp & \perp & \perp & \perp \\
\perp & \perp & \perp & \perp & \perp \\
\perp & \perp & \perp & \perp & \perp
\end{array}
\qquad
\begin{array}{ccc}
\propto & \propto & \propto
\end{array}
\qquad
\begin{array}{ccc}
a_{11}+b_{11}i & a_{12}+b_{12}i & a_{13}+b_{13}i \\
a_{21}+b_{21}i & a_{22}+b_{22}i & a_{23}+b_{23}i \\
a_{31}+b_{31}i & a_{32}+b_{32}i & a_{33}+b_{33}i
\end{array}
$$

When you arrange *numbers* (either real or complex) in this way, you can, of course, use them for anything you wish, but one of the most common uses is as a *matrix*—an array with mathematical rules and properties:

$$
\begin{bmatrix}
a_{11} & a_{12} & a_{13} & a_{14} \\
a_{21} & a_{22} & a_{23} & a_{24} \\
a_{31} & a_{32} & a_{33} & a_{34} \\
a_{41} & a_{42} & a_{43} & a_{44}
\end{bmatrix}
\begin{bmatrix}
x_1 \\ x_2 \\ x_3 \\ x_4
\end{bmatrix}
=
\begin{bmatrix}
b_1 \\ b_2 \\ b_3 \\ b_4
\end{bmatrix}
$$

Notice the numbering convention used in arrays: *element*$_{ij}$ is the element in the ith row, at the jth column. An $n \times m$ array is an array with n rows and m columns.

How does the 48 represent arrays?

The 48 can represent real-valued and complex-valued arrays and do many matrix operations on them. But because it also does non-matrix operations, the object type is called by its more general name—*array*.

The 48 uses double brackets to delimit the array itself—and single brackets to delimit each row within the array:

<table>
<tr><td>

```
[[ 1 1 ]]
```
1×2 real-valued array

</td><td>

```
[[ 1 2 3 ]
 [ 4 5 6 ]
 [ 7 8 9 ]]
```
3×3 real-valued array

</td></tr>
</table>

```
[[ (1,2) (-13.5,24.1) (4,-3.2) ]]
```
1×3 complex-valued array

<table>
<tr><td>

```
[[ -32.4 ]
 [ 15.6 ]
 [ 1.015 ]
 [ -19.623 ]]
```
4×1 real-valued array

</td><td>

```
[ -32.4 15.6 1.015 -19.623 ]
```
4-element vector

</td></tr>
</table>

Notice that these last two examples are actually different object *types* (the array, with its [[ ]] notation on the left; the vector, with its simpler [ ] on the right). But mathematically, they are treated the same by the 48 in many of its array/matrix operations. That is, a vector is actually a *1-column array,* displayed on its side for ease of viewing.

How do you build an array?

As usual, start with the basics—keying in the object at the Command Line. You key in arrays by *row*—a sequence called *row-major* order. Practice by keying in the examples on the previous page....

Go: Clear your Stack and go to STD mode, then: [←][[]][←][[]][1][SPC] [1][ENTER]. There's your **1×2** real-valued array.

Next: [←][[]][←][[]][1][SPC][2][SPC][3][▶][4][SPC][5][SPC][6][SPC][7][SPC][8] [SPC][9][ENTER]. There's your **3×3** real-valued array.

Notice how you use [▶] to skip over the closing bracket at the end of the first row in the array. And that's the only time you need to key in the inner brackets—around the first row. After that, as long as you enter the elements in row-major order, the 48 can arrange the remaining elements correctly—because it knows that all rows must have the same number of elements.

Continue: Go to rectangular mode ([→][POLAR]), if necessary, then [←][[]][←][[]][←][()][1][SPC][2][▶][←][()] [1][3][·][5][+/−][SPC][2][4][·][1][▶][←][()][4][SPC][3][·][2][+/−][ENTER]. There's your **1×3** complex-valued array.

And: [←][[]][←][[]][3][2][·][4][▶][1][5][·][6][SPC][1][·][0][1][5][SPC] [1][9][·][6][2][3][+/−][ENTER]. There's your **4×1** real-valued *array*;

Or: [←][[]][3][2][·][4][+/−][SPC][1][5][·][6][SPC][1][·][0][1][5][SPC][1][9][·] [6][2][3][+/−][ENTER]. There's your 4-element real-valued *vector*.

The Next Step: Build these same arrays from elements that you put onto the Stack first....

OK: Press ⊣(CLEAR) to clean the slate, then:
(1)(ENTER)(1)(ENTER)⊣({ })(1)(SPC)(2)(ENTER)(PRG) **TYPE** **→ARR** .
There's your **1×2** real-valued array.

As you'll recall from your practice with building vectors, the **→ARR** command takes the argument from Stack Level 1 and uses this to build an array or vector of the proper dimensions. To build a vector—whose dimensions are always $n{\times}1$—you use a real number argument (since only n needs to be specified). But to build an $n{\times}m$ array, you must specify both n and m in your argument—and you do this in a *list*.

Next: (1)(SPC)(2)(SPC)(3)(SPC)(4)(SPC)(5)(SPC)(6)(SPC)(7)(SPC)(8)(SPC)(9) (ENTER) (remember that you can line up several objects in the Command Line—separated by delimiting spaces like this— then (ENTER) them onto the Stack all at once). Now ⊣({ })(3)(SPC) (3)(ENTER) **→ARR** . There's your **3×3** real-valued array.

Then: ⊣(( ))(1)(SPC)(2)(ENTER)⊣(( ))(1)(3)(•)(5)(+/−)(SPC)(2)(4)(•)(1) (ENTER)⊣(( ))(4)(SPC)(3)(•)(2)(+/−)(ENTER)⊣({ })(1)(SPC)(3)(ENTER) **→ARR** . There's your **1×3** complex-valued array.

And: (3)(2)(•)(4)(+/−)(SPC)(1)(5)(•)(6)(SPC)(1)(•)(0)(1)(5)(SPC)(1)(9)(•)(6) (2)(3)(+/−)(ENTER). Then *either* ⊣({ })(4)(SPC)(1)(ENTER) **→ARR** —to build your **4×1** real-valued *array*; or (4) **→ARR** —to build your 4-element, real-valued *vector*. Try both. The *type* of argument (real or list) determines the type of object (vector or array).

No prizes for guessing what  does to arrays....

Try It: Press ▮OBJ→▮ and see that **4×1** array/vector decompose right before your eyes.... Notice, however, that the machine always puts the argument onto the Stack as a *list*—even if it's decomposing a vector. But the fact that there's just a single dimension in the list tells the machine that this is meant to build a vector rather than an array. Try ▮→ARR▮ now and watch it reconstruct....

In this way you can toggle back and forth all day between ▮→ARR▮ and ▮OBJ→▮. This is precisely the purpose of all of these object-building and decomposing functions: to let you quickly take an object apart, edit some or all of it, then rebuild the result with a minimum of hassle.

Feel free to (DROP) the **4×1** array off the Stack and observe ▮OBJ→▮ in action with some of the other arrays you still have hanging around up there....

Math with Arrays

The best thing about arrays is how easy it is to do matrix math....

To Wit: Let $A = \begin{bmatrix} 2 & 5 \\ 1 & 3 \end{bmatrix}$ and $C = \begin{bmatrix} 8 & 8 \\ 8 & 8 \end{bmatrix}$. If $2AB + C = 0$, find B.

                What if $C = \begin{bmatrix} -2 & 0 \\ 0 & -2 \end{bmatrix}$?

Too Easy: Solving for B gives $B=(A^{-1})(-C/2)$. So first, press ⇐(CLEAR) (MTH) █MATR█ █MAKE█. Here is where the matrix-building operations live.

            To build C, press ⇐[ ]⇐[ ]8(SPC)8▶8(SPC)8(ENTER) *or* ⇐{ }2(SPC)2(ENTER)8 █CON█ (the quick way to build a matrix filled with a CONstant value). Next, (+/–) to negate C (i.e. all its elements), then divide it by 2 ((2)(÷)). Now, the 48 knows that when you say $Y÷X$, what you really mean is $X^{-1}Y$. So *just divide by A*: ⇐[ ]⇐[ ]2(SPC)5 ▶1(SPC)3(÷)   <u>Result</u>: **[[8 8]**   This is B.
                                        [-4 -4]]

          Now, using $C =$ **[[-2 0]**   repeat the calculation.*
                       [0 -2]]

                 You should get $B =$ **[[3 -5]**
                             [-1 2]]

---

*And note that to build this value of C, you also have the █IDN█ command, which creates a multiplicative *identity* matrix (a square matrix with 1's on the diagonal)—provided that you tell it the size of the matrix. So you *could* build C as follows: (2) █IDN█ (2)(+/–)(×)

Flags

A flag is one of the simplest objects of all. It's just a single *bit*—a binary digit—that has just two possible values: 1 or 0. Using the 48's jargon, a flag is either *set* or *clear*. If you set a given flag, you turn that bit on (giving it a value of 1); if you clear it, you turn the bit off (giving it a value of 0).

How does the 48 represent flags?

Flags are indeed objects in the 48, but they're a little different than the other objects you've seen so far. First of all you don't *build* flags; they're already built. There are a fixed number of them—128—already identified by number and reserved in the machine (whereas, with other object types, you can build as many as you want).

Secondly, *some flags already have very specific meanings to the machine*—not so with the real numbers, vectors, or lists you might use in your calculations. Those objects' values have no preconceived significance to the 48; the values may be meaningful to *you*, causing you to change *your* behavior (e.g. answer a test question, redesign a bridge, etc.), but they don't cause the 48 to change *its* behavior (e.g. redefine the keyboard, change the display format, etc.). By contrast, fully half of the flags (numbered –1 to –64 and called *system flags*) are indeed dedicated to controlling parts of the 48 workshop itself, like operating lights on the wall that flip on/off as indicators of certain conditions (display modes, etc.). The other 64 flags (numbered 1 to 64 and called *user flags*) have no such prescribed meanings; they're left up to you to interpret—much like other object types.

The third big difference between flags and other objects is in their representation: they have none. That is, the 48 doesn't represent a flag "on the Stack." There's simply no delimiter (such as { } or [ ]) that means "this is a flag."

To "see" a flag, you must identify it by number and *inquire* as to its current value. The machine will then respond by putting either a 1 or 0 onto the Stack. But this response is just the machine's message to you—just a *real number* object—not the flag itself. You can change this response number however you want without affecting the flag; tearing up a sports page doesn't alter the outcome of the contests it reports.

Also, besides reporting the status of any flag you ask about, the 48 continually informs you of the states of certain flags—with annunciators in the Status Area. Several system flags are tied to the annunciators for angle mode and vector display mode. And, when set, *user* flags 1 through 5 display their numbers in the Status Area, too—just so you have a few flags of your own that you can monitor easily.

How do you control flags?

Of course, you can do more than just test flags (ask if they're set or clear); you can set or clear them yourself....

Watch: System flags −17 and −18 control the display's angle mode. When both these flags are *clear*, you're in degrees mode (as you should be now—press ⬅️RAD if necessary). But if only flag −17 is set, this sets RADians mode. Press PRG **TEST** NXT NXT. Here are your flag control functions.

As with all commands on the 48, you key in any necessary *argument* (in this case, that's the number of the flag) and then invoke the command. Thus, to use Set Flag (SF), you would press 1 7 +/− **SF** .... See? The **RAD** annunciator appears in the Status Area.

Now test flag −17 (i.e. ask if it's set): 1 7 +/− **FS?** .... The answer is 1 ("yes"). But ask a different question: "Is the flag *clear*?" 1 7 +/− **FC?** .... Of course, this answer is 0 ("no") —it's not clear. Now re-set degrees mode: 1 7 +/− **CF** .

You can set, clear and test *any* of the 128 flags. Try setting and clearing some user flags (if you're using just a few user flags, it's handiest to use the first five, because the Status Area informs you when they are set): 1 **SF** 2 **SF** 3 **SF** 4 **SF** 5 **SF** .... You get the idea (now be sure to clear those five flags—try this list shortcut: ⬅️{} 1 SPC 2 SPC 3 SPC 4 SPC 5 ENTER **CF**).

Flags aren't particularly useful from the keyboard. You'll use them most often within programs—to inquire of the current system states and to remember previous decisions and inputs—as you'll see later.

Here are some questions to consider, though:

Question: You know you can test or change the value of any single flag. Can you test or change the values of *all* flags?

Answer: Yes, you can test or adjust the values of all 128 flags or the 64 system flags—all at once (see p. 105).

Question: If you ask for the states of all 128 flags, what kind of response value could possibly represent this?

Answer: Since a flag is just a single bit, you'd need a value that contained multiple bits—a *binary integer*. That's the object type you're going to study next. The results of your multiple flag test (via a command called RCLF— "ReCalL Flags") will be such a binary integer. And the argument you give to simultaneously *alter* the values of a group of flags (via a command called STOF—"STOre Flags") will also be a binary integer.

Now, if you stop and think about it, you'll realize that RCLF and STOF lets you preserve *in a different object type*—a binary integer—exact "blueprints" of all the flag settings at *any* given time. So although you can have only 128 flag states at once, *there's no limit to the number of such "blueprints" you can save and later transplant as necessary.*

Binary Integers

All right—now for binary integers. A binary integer is an ordered collection of flags, or *bits*. And, like other object types, the binary integer object has its own set of rules for manipulating and interpreting this collection.

First of all, the reason it's called an integer is that its list of bits is most commonly used to *represent integer values*. The integer may vary length from 1 to 64 bits. For example, here's an 8-bit binary integer:

$$0\ 0\ 1\ 0\ 1\ 1\ 0\ 0$$

The integer value these bits form is commonly expressed in any of four convenient number *bases:*

00101100_2 (base 2 or *binary* format)

54_8 (base 8 or *octal* format)

44_{10} (base 10 or *decimal* format—which you know and love)

$2C_{16}$ (base 16 or *hexadecimal* format)

How does the 48 represent binary integers?

The 48 can express binary integer values in any of those four bases, but its display doesn't accommodate subscripts very well, so it represents a binary integer on the Stack beginning with a pound sign, # (to signal that it's a binary integer) and ending with either b, o, d or h—to indicate which _base_ it's using to _format_ the value:

`# 101100b`   `# 54o`   `# 44d`   `# 2Ch`

Do This: Build a binary integer with the above value (there's only one value represented there), and then view it in each of those four formats.

Like So: Press (MTH), then **BASE**, and notice the first four items on that menu. _The base currently in use will be the interpretation the 48 puts on any value you key in with a_ #. For example, press **OCT**, then (→)(#)(1)(ENTER)....

Nothing to it, right? And now you can view this value in any of the other three base formats also: Press **BIN** ...; press **HEX** ...; press **DEC** .... Simple.

All right, now how do you change the number of bits in a binary integer? As you read, you can have anywhere from 1 to 64 bits.

Simple: Change the current *word size*—the maximum number of bits allowed in the integer. For instance, to change the word size to 8, you would press ⑧ (there's the *argument* of the command), then (NXT) **STWS** (there's the command). And you can check the current word size any time you want, too—with **RCWS** (try it now).... The 48 answers your question with the appropriate real number.

The largest value you can represent in 8 bits is # 11111111b, which is # 255d. So, what if you try to key in a value larger than this, say, # 256d?

Press ((NXT) **DEC** , if necessary) (→)#②⑤⑥(ENTER)....Hmm. You get: # 0d Why? Because # 256d is # 100000000b, which takes nine bits to represent. But you've told the 48—via the word size—that you want to use only the first (*right-most*) eight bits (00000000), which form the value # 0d.

Good news: That ninth bit is actually still there. Press ⑨ (NXT) **STWS** and "thar she blows"—the complete number (go back to an 8-bit word size and do this change while watching in binary format, too).

Want to see how the flags look when you use RCLF to put their aggregate values onto the Stack as binary integers?

OK: Change the current word size to 64 (press ⑥④ ▆▆▆▆). And to make the values easier to comprehend, use decimal formatting (press ▆▆▆▆, if necessary). Now, execute the RCLF command: ⓐⓐⓇⒸⓁⒻ ⒺⓃⓉⒺⓇ.... You should* get this list:

{ # 316659348800496 # 0d }

The first number is the aggregate binary-integer value of all 64 system flags; the second is the aggregate binary-integer value of your 64 user flags. These two values represent the entire "blueprint" of the machine's status and your own flag settings.

Now, holding your place here, look back at page 11. That preparatory exercise you performed before starting the Course was simply a setting of all flags to their *clear* states—so both the two desired values were given as **# 0**. You did this mass flag adjustment with the STOF command—do it again now:

⬅ { } ➡ # 0 ➡ # 0 ⒺⓃⓉⒺⓇ ⓐⓐⓈⓉⓄⒻ ⒺⓃⓉⒺⓇ

If you give STOF a single binary integer value (not a list), this will adjust only the 64 *system* flags: # 0 ⓐⓐⓈⓉⓄⒻ ⒺⓃⓉⒺⓇ

---

*If you don't get these values, don't worry. It just means one of the your display settings or angle modes or something like that is set differently than assumed here. No problem—you're going to reset them here anyway.

Math and logic with binary integers

The principal reason you have binary integers is so that you can do digital math and logic operations—the stuff so near and dear to the hearts of computer scientists. Don't worry—you're not going to explore all the bit manipulations and logical operations the BASE menu offers (if you need them, then you already know what they're good for, and you don't need an Easy Course to tell you).

But it's good for everybody to see a little bit of integer arithmetic in action—just so you understand some of the 48's rules.

Example: What's $125_{10} + ABC_{16}$ expressed in 64-bit decimal?

Solution: Press 6 4 █STWS█ NXT 1 2 5 ENTER █HEX█ ↱ # α α A B C α + █DEC█ .... <u>Answer:</u> **# 2873d** As you can see, you can combine a real number with a binary integer. The result is a binary integer in the same base. To make this possible, the machine transforms the real number into a binary integer first—with the █R→B█ command ("Real-to-Binary", which you'll find, with its counterpart, █B→R█, there on the BASE menu). Of course, you can also use █R→B█ "manually" on a real number, but the 48 is smart enough to do it for you here. Be aware that █R→B█ *rounds* fractional portions of the real number, and it takes negative numbers to be 0. And any value requiring a binary representation larger than the current word size is silently truncated.

Example: What's $125_{10} - ABC_{16}$ expressed in 64-bit decimal?

Solution: Press ①②⑤ ENTER ⤵# α α A B C ⤺ H α ⊟ ....
<u>Answer</u>: # 18446744073709548993d

Notice that you can key in the base identifier (h here) directly—without switching to that display mode.

Why this huge answer? Why not # -2623d ?
Because instead of subtracting a binary integer, the 48 adds its *2's-complement*.*

Example: What are $258_{10} \times 3_{10}$ and $258_{10} \div 3_{10}$ computed in 8-bit decimal?

Solutions: NXT ⑧ STWS ⤵# ②⑤⑧ ENTER ③ ✕   <u>Answer</u>: # 6d
⤵# ②⑤⑧ ENTER ③ ÷   <u>Answer</u>: # 0d

The 48 actually *truncates* (to the current word size) any value you use in arithmetic. Thus the above multiplication was actually $2_{10} \times 3_{10}$. And the division was actually $2_{10} \div 3_{10}$ (binary division remainders are dropped).

That's different than if you did the division with reals and then limited the word size in the result. And you can do just that with the R→B (Real-to-Binary) command in the BASE menu: ②⑤⑧ ENTER ③ ÷ NXT R→B .

---

*Complementing is the computer scientist's method for carrying and borrowing and negation during arithmetic with binary integers. If you don't already know how complementing works, you probably don't need to worry about it.

Character Strings

Character strings are just that—strings of characters (letters, numbers, symbols—basically, anything you can type):

ABCDEF_XYZ   12345   #~$@&(%)?!   3.1416+pi=oops

Within such strings, characters have no numeric or other quantitative or special significance; they're just characters. A string may have several characters, one character, or even none at all.

How does the 48 represent character strings?

Often called simply *strings*, character strings on the 48 appear within quotation marks, " ", as if to say that the enclosed characters are to be taken literally, with no further interpretation:

      `"ABCDEF_XYZ"`   `"12345"`

      `"#~$@&(%)?!"`   `"3.1416+pi=oops"`

The main purpose of strings is to let you store and manipulate verbal information. For example, you can use strings to put together results such as `"The answer is no."` and `"The AREA is 2.5_ft"`, thus making your calculations more meaningful and complete than just unadorned numeric results. And then there's textual information—the kind of "stuff" that can be represented only by character strings: names and addresses, etc.

How do you build a string?

Begin as usual....

Type It: Try building the four strings on the opposite page.

Like So: ⬅CLEAR ➡["] α α A B C D E F ➡_ X Y Z ENTER; ➡["] 1 2 3 4 5 ENTER; then ➡["] α α ➡# ➡V ⬅4 ➡ENTER ⬅ENTER ⬅( ) ➡U α ▶ α α ⬅← ⬅DEL ENTER; then ➡["] 3 · 1 4 1 6 α α + ⬅ α P] ⬅= O O P S ENTER;

No big mysteries, right?* But remember: no matter what *numerals* you see within strings (as with the "12345"), they're *not* numbers.

Then: Guess how you can build strings from other Stack values?

Hmm: Press +....Two strings "add" (append) to one another just like two lists do (recall page 77). Press DROP, then 6 7 +.... When you "add" other object types** to a string, the machine converts those objects to their *string representations*** and then *appends* these to the existing string. Try ⬅[ ] 1 SPC 2 ENTER SWAP +.... The order matters—again, just as with lists.

---

*Though it was a bit of a refresher in Command Line typing. Do you remember how to find non-letter characters and type in lowercase, etc.? If not, look back at pages 31-39.

**except lists—you can't + them to strings (you'll add the string to the list instead).

***The string representations of some objects are slightly different than the objects themselves.

Of course, you can also convert objects to strings "manually"—instead of letting the machine do it—during a concatenation (appending).

Try It: Press (PRG) **TYPE**. Key in, say, a vector: (←)[ ][ ]2 (SPC)2 7 (SPC)5 (ENTER). Now convert this into a string, by pressing **→STR** (it simply wraps this object in quotes, thus transforming its type into a string.... Now concatenate this to the string above it: (+).

As you might suspect from all this object conversion, a string is only slightly less "general" an object type than a list. So it's almost as important to know how to take strings apart as to build them....

Do This: Remember the All-Purpose Object Dissector? Try it now (press **OBJ→**)....See what happens?

When a string contains representations of other objects, the machine will extract them, one by one (from left to right), and put them onto the Stack—just as if they had been (ENTER)'ed from the Command Line without quotation marks. But remember, too, that a string can contain anything else too—*besides* syntactically correct object representations. Therefore **OBJ→** can often give you errors as the machine tries to make an object out of characters in the string that were never meant for such.

Then: Press (ENTER) to make a copy of the vector now at Level 1. Then ▸STR (ENTER) and (NXT), to go to the next page of the TYPE menu.

Example: Type (α)(α)(S)(I)(Z)(E)(ENTER). The number you get, 10, tells you how many characters were in "[2 27 5]". Now (◀), (▶), and use SIZE on the *vector* [2 27 5] instead. The result is { 3 }, right? There are three elements in the vector, so its SIZE appears in this single-element *list* —just as if you had used OBJ▸ to break it down into its components (recall page 90).   Now press (◀).

Question: Recall page 35. The 48 can display 256 different characters, but not all are available on keys. Can you put them into strings without using the CHARS menu?

Answer: Yes. Each character has an associated number—a character code that represents the character. NUM returns the character code of the *first character* of a given string. Try NUM now and see 91, which is the code for the [character. Then use CHR to confirm this—converting from the code back to the character.

Of course, there's certainly a lot more you can do with strings—just as with all the other objects—but at least you get the idea here.

Tags

Just as real numbers are linked together to build complex numbers and arrays—and just as bits form flags or binary integers—so too can strings be the simpler building blocks of other, "hybrid" object types. One simple one is a tag.

A tag is a pairing of a string with another object (any type) on the Stack so that the string forms a *temporary label*. Your workbench can get pretty "Stacked" up with objects, and so it's difficult to keep track of them all and remember what meant what. Tags are a harmless, temporary way to help you do this.

                         ③ OBJECTS: YOUR RAW MATERIALS

How does the 48 represent tags?

You don't build a tag by itself. As the name implies, you attach it to some other object—so it's more meaningful to ask "How does the 48 represent tagged objects?"

On the Stack, they might look, for example, like these:

```
Root: -1           Extrm: (0,-1)

Zero: 0            Unit: [ 0.27 0.53 0.80 ]
```

The tag itself is everything to the left of (and including) the colon. To the right of the colon is the object being tagged

How do you build a tag?

First—as always—you can simply type it in.

Thus: [→][::][α][α][R][←][α][O][O][T][α][▶][1][+/−][ENTER].

> Notice that the displayed version of a tag has one colon—to save space in the display. But you must *enclose* the tag (*both* sides) with colons when you type it in, so use [▶] to skip over the second **:** before typing the object—just as you do when starting a new row of elements in an array.

That's how to build a tag when you key in an object, but most of the time you'll want to tag an object that's already on the Stack.

Well, you can't put a tag by itself on the Stack. A tag is just a string until it is attached to another object. Fortunately the tag-attachment tool, **→TAG**, is right there on the first page of the PRG TYPE menu.

Try This: Press ←CLEAR, then put −1 onto the Stack: 1 +/− ENTER. Suppose that's the result of some calculation, and now, afterwards, you want to label it with a tag. Just key in the tag, as a string: → "" α α R ← α O O T ENTER. Then use **→TAG**. The result is the same as before.

And Also: You can use real numbers as tags. Suppose you're a land surveyor who deals with coordinates all day long. Each point in a survey might have an identifying number—a tag—attached to the vector coordinate pair itself:

Press ← [ ] 1 5 0 · 2 3 SPC 6 5 · 7 9 ENTER.... There are your coordinates. Now label it with some identifying number: 1 2 **→TAG**. The 48 actually converts the real number to a string and then uses this as the tag.

As Usual: You can break up a tagged object into its object and its tag string, by using the General Purpose Object De-composer, **OBJ→**. Try it now....
Now **→TAG** to rebuild the tagged object.

How do you use tags?

Tags are indeed _temporary_ labels. If you do any operation on a tagged object, the 48 will remove and discard the tag. After all, the result of the operation isn't generally the same object as before.

Watch: Try adding another vector to the tagged vector now sitting at Level 1: ⬅[ ][1][0][SPC][2][0][+].... See what happens? The vector addition works just fine, but the tag on the previous object goes away.

Try another: multiply the Root: -1 by this result vector: [×].... Again, the math works fine, but the tag doesn't stick to the result.

As you saw with that surveyor's scenario, you can use real numbers as tags to index multiple results of the same kind (e.g. the points in the surveyor example). Or—more commonly—you use a string to give it some kind of temporary label of characters.

No matter what, a tag is the most fragile of objects—as you can see from above. Any meaningful operation of the object will "rip the tag off." A tag is for your benefit only; it doesn't mean anything to the machine. So the best use for tags is at the end of programs or other calculations, when you can attach them and display finished results.

Names

By contrast to tags, a name in the 48 is a much more "solid" kind of label. Names are very important, because they identify *places* where objects are stored. Names are like *labelled boxes* in your workshop. When you want to "use an object," you simply *invoke* (type) its name.

That goes for all the built-in objects, too. Every command (every key and menu item) is an object of some type, and when you press its key, this actually *invokes* ("types") the object's *built-in* name. For example, when you press the [SIN] key, you are invoking the *name*, SIN, which is the built-in (permanently labelled) box containing the sine program.

Well, building your own names is simply the act of creating new storage boxes with your own labels on them. Once you've done that, the names exist; you can put them onto the Stack, move them around, etc.—just like other objects—even when they're empty. But, of course, they're usually more useful when you do store objects in them. So here's where you start learning how to do that—how to save the objects you build....

How does the 48 represent names?

A name is simply a character string with special restrictions on the characters allowed. Examples:

    'A'   'EX1'   'Tuesday'   'ΣDAT'   'PPAR'

          'Whatchamacallit'   'SINx'

How do you build a name?

Build the first couple of names you see above.

Easy: Press `'` `α` `A` `ENTER`; press `'` `α` `E` `α` `X` `1` `ENTER`; and so on—you get the idea. The `'` `'` delimiters appear in pairs—just like so many others you've seen by now.

As you can see, names are always enclosed in *apostrophes* (`'` `'`)rather than quotes (`"` `"`)—to distinguish them from normal character strings. Also, names have these special restrictions:

* You cannot use any *delimiter* in a name: #, ', ", _, :, (), [], {}, «», ∢, , , \<space\> and \<newline\> are all off limits.

* Numerals (0-9) and decimal points are OK, *except* as the first character: You can use 'A1' and 'Hi.', but not '1A' or '.WP'.

* No arithmetic symbols or operators! Names like 'A+B' are out.

* You can't create a name that's already used by a *built-in* command: 'SIN' is the *built-in name* for the sine function; 'SINx' is not.

How do you use a name?

To put something into a named box, you use [STO] (STOre).

Watch: Press [1][ENTER][']["α][A][STO]....

You just stored the real number **1** into the name **'A'**.

Notice the order of the objects: First you put the *object to be stored* onto the workbench. Then you put the *name* (that labelled storage box). Then the STO command puts the object into the box, takes the filled box off the Stack and puts it into storage.

Question: *"...into storage"*—where's that?

Answer: It's in your own personal toolbox—the VAR menu. To get to it, simply press [VAR] (do this now)....

This is the menu of all the names that you've filled with objects (i.e. STOred objects into). As you can see, **A** is now the left-most box because it's the most recently filled; anything else you've stored (if anything) is bumped farther to the right in the menu.

It's called the VARiable menu because a *variable* is exactly that—a name labelling and containing some value, which can be changed (i.e. it can *vary*).

Once you've named an object, to use it you simply refer to it by name.

Look: Type ⍺ A ENTER....

Result: You get the *value* in '**A**', which is the real number, 1.

This is the general rule: Whenever you type the name of an object you are *invoking* that name. The machine will *evaluate* the object for you—*exactly as if you had typed the object itself from the Command Line* (i.e. as if you had typed 1 ENTER here).

And: Press the ▮**A**▮ item on the VAR menu.... Same thing, right? Again—as you read earlier—pressing a VARiable key is just a shortcut for *typing that name*.

But: Type ' ⍺ A ENTER (or ' ▮**A**▮ ENTER)....

Result: You don't get the *value* in '**A**'—only its *name*.

This is just what you saw when creating names (page 117): The ' means that you simply want to put the name onto the Stack. Maybe you're building a new name; maybe you want to STOre a new value into an existing name—whatever.

It's a very important point—worth "harping on" once more:

- To put just the *name* onto the Stack, enclose it in ' marks.

- To *invoke* the name—i.e. to get the *value* it contains— use it *without* ' marks.

Question: What if you have a name on the Stack and *then* you decide that you want to evaluate it?

No Sweat: To *evaluate* a name already on the Stack, simply press [EVAL].... See? It EVALuates the name ' Я '.

By the way, notice this: Evaluating a name always gets you a *copy* of its object's value. Thus, you can evaluate the name over and over again—using and consuming the resulting values on the Stack—but the original object stays safely in its labelled box.

Clean Up: Press [←][CLEAR]['][Я] (a menu key is just a shortcut for typing, right?). Now [←][PURG].... [Я] disappears from your VAR menu; you PURGe'd it from your toolbox—both the name and the object it contained.

Now: What will happen if you try to invoke the name Я? Hmm—there's no such name, right? Try it: Press [α][A][ENTER]....

You get the name: ' Я '   How? And why?

Because whenever you *invoke* a name—any name—the 48 actually puts ' marks around it and puts the name onto the Stack first. *Then* it performs an EVAL on it. If the name contains any other object, then of course, you'll get that object's value. But if the name contains no other object, *it uses its own object value* (after all, a name is an object, too—right?).

③ OBJECTS: YOUR RAW MATERIALS

Practice some more: Store some objects and evaluate some names....

Example: Store the vector [1 2 3] in the name 'Vector.1'

Solution: Press ⇦CLEAR to clear distractions, then ⇦[]1SPC
2SPC3ENTER'ααV⇦αECTOR.1αSTO.
Now look in your VAR menu. The left-most box is **VECTO**.
Did the 48 truncate (and capitalize) the name you keyed
in—just to fit it into the display's menu box?

To find out, press '**VECTO**.... Nope—the 48 knows and
remembers the entire actual name; it simply needs to
alter it for its menu boxes. So keep your names short and
distinct! *Each menu box holds only up to 5 characters—
and uppercase always.* So any similar (yet completely
valid) names such as 'Vector.1' and 'Vector.2' or
'VECT' and 'Vect' will *appear* identical in the menu.

Question: Can you store a name within a name? It seems reasonable. After all, you can put one box containing an object
into another box, right? Try it—store 1 in 'B' and 'B'
in 'A': CANCEL1'αBSTO' **B** ENTER'αASTO.

OK, But: *What will you get* now when you invoke (*evaluate*) the
name A? Press **A**.... You get 1! So the EVALuation
process *goes all the way:* If the value of one name is yet
another name, the 48 then evaluates *that* name, and so
on—down to the last "box within a box within a box...".

So evaluation is really a chain of evaluations—as long as necessary:*
The 48 follows its nose through each name, evaluating its contents—
until finally it finds the value of the "innermost" object.

Problem: What if you're interested in a name's actual contents only—the object immediately "inside" the name? That is, you don't want the 48 to evaluate *that* object any further—just put it on the Stack. How do you do this?

Solution: Use RCL to recall the contents of 'A': ['] [A] [→][RCL]....
You get 'B'—the actual contents of 'A'. Because you *recalled* the contents of 'A' (rather than evaluating it), the 48 did *not* go on to evaluate those contents. And note that RCL is a *copying* process: the object in 'A' (the name 'B') is still in 'A' (try ['] [A] [→][RCL] again).

So [STO] and [→][RCL] form a kind of matched set:

- To STOre an object into a name, you put the object onto the Stack, then the name, then press [STO]. The STOrage process *consumes* both object and name—it's *not* a copying process (the object is taken as the original, and no duplicate is left on the Stack).

- To ReCaLl the object, you put the name onto the Stack. Then you use [→][RCL] and you get (a *copy* of) the object back on the Stack.

*Up to the memory of the machine, of course. And beware of circular references: If you were to store 'A' into 'B' right now, then 'A' would contain 'B' and 'B' would contain 'A'. And M.C. Escher would love such a conundrum—but your 48 wouldn't. It would evaluate in a circle, and you'd need to press [CANCEL] to interrupt this infinite goose-chase. The 48 can actually catch self-referencing names (i.e. storing 'A' into 'A') and give you a message, Error: Circular Reference.

[3] OBJECTS: YOUR RAW MATERIALS

In fact, STO and RCL are so useful that the VAR menu offers a shortcut:

This: Press ⟨←⟩(CLEAR), then ⟨4⟩⟨←⟩■ **N** ■. Now press ⟨→⟩■ **N** ■....

You just did this: ⟨←⟩(CLEAR)⟨4⟩(')■ **N** ■(STO)(')■ **N** ■(→)(RCL).

Using a VAR menu key *by itself* will *evaluate* the name.
Using (') first simply *types* the name onto the Command Line.
Using ⟨←⟩ first STOres the Level-1 object into that name.
Using ⟨→⟩ first ReCaLLs a copy of the actual object in the name.

Of course, once you recall the contents of a name to the Stack, you might want to alter it. But how?

Easy: EDIT it! For example, to change the first value in **Vector.1** to **10**: (→)**VECTO** (recall its current value), then ⟨←⟩(EDIT)(►)(►)(►)(0) (ENTER)(EDIT that object), and ⟨←⟩**VECTO** (store this new version back into the name '**Vector.1**'). *Remember:* EDITing alters only a copy of the contents of a name on the Stack. It does *not* automatically STOre the EDITed version back into that name.

So: To recall, edit *and* restore a named object in one smooth motion, use EDIT on the *name* of the object: Change that vector component back to **1**: (')**VECTO**(ENTER)⟨←⟩(EDIT)(►)(►)(►)(◄)(1)(ENTER). See? This lets you skip the RCL and the STO.*

---

*And in case of mistakes during "alterations," remember that (CANCEL) aborts an EDIT.

Algebraic Objects

Algebra is the branch of mathematics that manipulates expressions and equations involving *variables*—"unidentified numbers" that can nevertheless be manipulated as symbols because their numerical *properties* are known and predictable:

$$x^2 + y^2 = r^2 \qquad\qquad ax^2 + bx + c = 0$$

The beauty of algebra is that you can manipulate the symbols into the most advantageous arrangement—before ever worrying about the numerical values these symbols might represent.

$$y = \sqrt{r^2 - x^2} \qquad\qquad x = \frac{-b \pm \sqrt{b^2 - 4ac}}{2a}$$

Then you can "plug in" numerical values:

$$y = \sqrt{5^2 - 4^2} \qquad\qquad x = \frac{-10 \pm \sqrt{10^2 - 4(3)(3)}}{2(3)}$$

Well, it's no coincidence that your menu of named objects in the 48 is called a VARiable menu: *You can use names in the 48 literally as algebraic symbols,* to form algebraic expressions and equations (such as those above) that you manipulate and solve *symbolically.* And just like algebra on paper, you needn't worry about the actual, numerical values in those variables until you're ready to "plug them in!"

How does the 48 represent algebraic objects?

As you know, you can't use math operators (e.g. $+$ $-$ $*$ $/$) as characters in names. If you do, you'll form an algebraic object instead. _Names_ and _algebraic objects use the same delimiter_ (**'**).

Examples: At your VAR menu, press ⟦'⟧⟦ █ ⟧⟦ENTER⟧. That's a name. Press ⟦'⟧⟦ █ ⟧⟦ENTER⟧. That's another name. But press ⟦'⟧⟦ █ ⟧⟦+⟧⟦ █ ⟧⟦ENTER⟧. That's an _algebraic object._ You built it by typing a mathematically meaningful _combination_ of names and algebraic operations.

And of course, you can edit this object—just like any other: ⟦←⟧⟦EDIT⟧⟦SKIP⟧⟦◄⟧⟦−⟧⟦α⟧⟦C⟧⟦ENTER⟧. <u>Result</u>: 'A+B−C'

So you can always type in an algebraic object at the Command Line—using whatever combinations of VAR and alphabetic keys that are most convenient. But often it's easier to let the Stack's postfix operations actually help you build an algebraic object:

Watch: ⟦DROP⟧ the 'A+B−C', then press ⟦+⟧.... See what happens? Just as ⟦+⟧ lets you combine lists or strings, so it combines names and algebraic objects into larger algebraic objects.

Try another: Key in the name 'C' (press ⟦'⟧⟦α⟧⟦C⟧⟦ENTER⟧), then ⟦−⟧.... Voilá!

How do you use algebraic objects?

"Ah—how sweet it is!..."

Question: _What's going to happen_ now if you EVALuate this algebraic object, 'A+B-C' ? Press (EVAL).... Result: '5-C'. Why? Because _the machine evaluates everything in the expression that it can_ (the variable names 'A' and 'B' have the values 4 and 1 stored in them); _but it leaves any undefined value as is—in symbolic form_ (the name 'C' contains nothing—it's not on your VAR menu).*

Do This: Evaluate the algebraic object 'A+B'.
Press (') A (+) B (ENTER) (or (') A (ENTER) (') B (ENTER)(+)—your choice), then (EVAL)....   Result: 5
This result is _not_ an algebraic object—it's a real number—because all the parts of 'A+B' are numerically evaluable; it has no undefined names (such as 'C').

One More: Evaluate 'A*Vector.1': (') A (×)(VECTO)(ENTER)
(or (') A (ENTER)(')(VECTO)(ENTER)(×)), then (EVAL)....
Result: [4 8 12]   Isn't this great?

---

* Notice that this exactly matches how the 48 EVALuates names: If a name has an object stored in it, the 48 evaluates that object; if not, _the name itself becomes the final object value._

Question: How do you know this last answer is correct? That is, how can you verify the current values of your VARiables 'A' and 'Vector.1'?

Answer(s): An easy way is simply to *evaluate* 'A' and 'Vector.1', by pressing ▮ A ▮ and ▮VECTO▮. You should get, respectively: 4 and [1 2 3].

Or, to review the values in *all* the names on the current page of your VAR menu, press →VIEW:

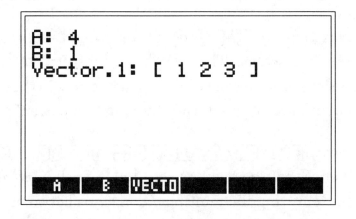

→VIEW is especially handy when you want to check a lot of values at once—but you don't want to mess up the Stack with name evaluations. Notice that the entire view is just a large message that appears temporarily over the normal Stack display (press CANCEL to clear it).

For practice with a more complicated example, try using an algebraic object to build one of the general solutions to a quadratic equation:

$$x = \frac{-b \pm \sqrt{b^2 - 4ac}}{2a}$$

Go: First, press ◁[CLEAR] to tidy up. Now start building:

Press ['][α]◁[B][ENTER][+/−]. <u>Result</u>: '−b'   So far, so good. Again, you're doing a mathematical operation on an algebraic object, and the object changes to reflect that operation.

Next, press [ENTER][+/−] (no sense keying 'b' in again from scratch; this is quicker). Then [2][yˣ].... <u>Result</u>: 'b^2' Because the 48 can't display superscripts in the Stack, it uses the circumflex (^) to indicate "raising to a power." *

Next, [4]['][α]◁[A][ENTER][×]['][α]◁[C][ENTER][×]....<u>Result</u>: '4*a*c' Notice that the result is *not* '4ac'. Such *implied* multiplication (i.e. omitting the multiplication signs between single-character variables—often used in written algebra) would confuse algebraic objects with *names* on the 48 Stack: 'xy', 'abc', etc.

Now [−], to form   'b^2-4*a*c'   *Notice* how the 48's postfix subtraction rule ("Level 2 minus Level 1") determines the order of the subtraction operation formed inside the algebraic object.**

*You could have typed ◁[x²] instead of [2][yˣ], but the result, 'SQ(b)', isn't quite as readable. Either form is OK, though—they both evaluate the same way.

**Notice also that you don't need any parentheses here: Under conventional algebraic notation (which the 48 uses), exponentiation takes precedence over multiplication/division, which takes precedence over addition/subtraction.

Next step: ⌐x⌐.... You get `'√(b^2-4*a*c)'`
Notice the parentheses. A one-line algebraic object can't draw the radical to include an entire expression under it. Instead, the square root is represented as a mathematical function (as in $f(x)$), and the parentheses enclose the argument of the function: √( )

Now press ⊕. Result: `'-b+√(b^2-4*a*c)'`
No surprises, right?

Keep going: ⓶ ⎘ α ← Ⓐ ENTER ⌐x⌐.... Result: `'2*a'`
Nothing unusual here, either—but by now you may have noticed something that's worth a little discussion: Normally, when doing Stack arithmetic with something like real numbers, you could just press ⓶ ENTER ⓷ ⌐x⌐. Here, you need a second ENTER, to put the `'a'` onto the Stack before multiplying. This is because when you press ⎘, the 48 goes into algebraic entry mode (the **ALG** annunciator appears in the Status Area), so that operations such as ⌐x⌐ are *not executed immediately*. Instead, they're simply typed (*, +, etc.) onto the Command Line. Therefore, you could also key in the expression `'2*a'` as ⎘ ⓶ ⌐x⌐ α ← Ⓐ ENTER, rather than build it via Stack operations.

Finally, press ⌐÷⌐.... Result: `'(-b+√(b^2-4*a*c))/(2*a)'`
Since algebraic objects are represented in a line on the Stack, the extra parentheses are needed to show what's being divided by what. Indeed, without them you'd have `'-b+√(b^2-4*a*c)/2*a'`, which, according to the notational conventions, would be evaluated as

$$-b + \left(\frac{\sqrt{b^2 - 4ac}}{2}\right)a$$

Some observations:

When building expressions involving your variable names, you began each name with ' , to tell the machine that you were merely *spelling out* the name as part of this object, not *evaluating* it. But if you *know* that the names you're using are empty (i.e. they're not on your VAR list—either you've PURGEd them or never used them before), then you can get away *without* the ' —because evaluating an *empty* name just gives you that name anyway.

Of course, you could have typed in the entire object directly from the Command Line: ['] [←] [(] [)] [+/–] [α] [←] [α] [α] B [+] [√x] [←] [(] [)] [α] B [y^x] [2] [–] [4] [×] [α] [A] [×] [α] [C] [▶] [▶] [÷] [←] [(] [)] [2] [×] [α] [A] [ENTER].

Admittedly, this saves some [ENTER]'s—and you can use lower-case lock ([←] [α] in alpha mode) to make it easier to type a, b, and c. But it also means you have to know where all the parentheses go *before you start*. And so you must know and follow the algebraic syntax and precedence conventions—instead of letting the 48 put it together for you "on the fly," as you simply specify the order of operations with the postfix Stack operations. So *you* decide—use the method easiest for you.

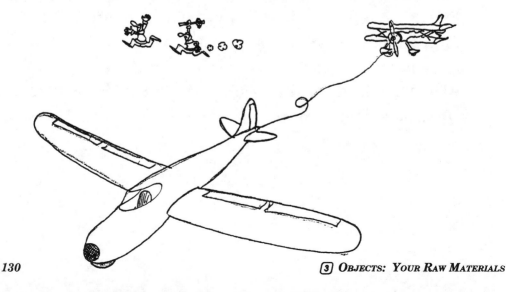

③ OBJECTS: *YOUR RAW MATERIALS*

No matter how you've built it, now that you have such an impressive algebraic object all built, what do you do with it?

This: Put values into the variables and evaluate the expression:

(VAR) (') (α) (E) (α) (Q) (STO)   (1) (') (α) (←) (C) (STO)
(2) (+/−) (') (α) (←) (B) (STO)   (1) (') (α) (←) (A) (STO)   **EQ** (EVAL)

You've just stored your freshly-built algebraic object into the name 'EQ'. Then you stored 1 into 'a', -2 into 'b', and 1 into 'c' (in reverse order—to appear in order in the menu*).

Then you put the expression back on the Stack by pressing **EQ**, thus *evaluating* the name 'EQ'. Then you evaluated the expression, and you got the real result.

> *"Hmm...but why doesn't the EVALuation process 'go all the way,' and evaluate the algebraic object?"*

It's an exception to the "EVALuate-all-the-way" rule: If a name contains an algebraic object, the 48 evaluates only to that object; you must press (EVAL) explicitly to evaluate the algebraic any more. So you did—and zap—the machine replaced all names with their values and did the math. And as with all evaluations, the result was left on the Stack: 1

Anyway, the **beauty** of such algebraic objects is this: Now you have your algebraic expression named, *you can easily reuse it.* For example:

(2) (←) **A** (1) (5) (+/−) (←) **B** (4) (←) **C** **EQ** (EVAL). <u>Result:</u> 7.22...

*Remember that they will appear in *uppercase* in the menu boxes—but you know they're the boxes farther to the *left* because they've been more recently created than the boxes for 'A' and 'B'.

Postfix Programs

When you say the word *program,* you probably think of some task or series of tasks that you "record" in a computer now and then "play back" later—at which time the machine *automatically* performs those tasks. The power of a program is that you can play the recording over and over with very little effort on your part every time—often the touch of a single key. *It can become a new tool in your workshop.*

Well, that's a fair way to think about a program. But then that means that *algebraic objects* are really *programs* of a sort. Look at how much work the machine does automatically when you press the (EVAL) key with an algebraic object: It evaluates all the names, then uses the math to combine them as you've specified—and it will do this over and over, for whatever values of variables you wish to give it.

You could make a similar argument for simply EVALuating a series of "names within names," too: That chain of evaluations can go on a long time—a very convenient series of tasks the machine does for you automatically. And, as you'll soon see, you can even get the 48 to sequentially evaluate the objects contained in a *list object* ({   })—again, simply by pressing that all-powerful (EVAL) key.

The point is, although there are several different types of objects that can act as programs, they have other roles as well. In fact, there's only one object type that was defined *strictly* for the purpose of acting as such a pre-recorded, ready-to-use series of commands. This is the object type called a *postfix program.*

How does the 48 represent postfix programs?

A postfix program (you can call it simply "program" for short), is indeed an object; you can put it onto the Stack, store (name) it, recall it and evaluate it. And, as with most other objects in your workshop, programs are bracketed by a pair of distinctive delimiters—in this case, guillemots: « »

Also true to the pattern of other objects is the program's underlying list-like structure: A program is an ordered collection of zero or more elements (objects and commands). When you evaluate the program, it sequentially evaluates its elements.

How do you build a postfix program?

Unlike most other objects, there is only one way to create a program, and that's to type it in from the Command Line.

Try One: Press ⏎« »①SPC②⊞ENTER. Result: « 1 2 + »

Notice that _program entry mode_ activates (i.e. the **PRG** annunciator appears in the Status Area) when you press « »—so that commands such as ⊞ simply type their names in the Command Line rather than executing immediately.

So there you have it—a three-step program.

Question: What does it do?

Answer: See for yourself: It's called a *postfix* program because *it handles objects and commands in the same manner as your 48's postfix Stack would handle them as you key them in on the Command Line.* So you can mimic this program's behavior at the Command Line: [1][SPC][2][+].*

Now [DROP] this "manual" result, then press [ENTER] once (to DUPlicate the program so you don't need to rebuild it later), and [EVAL]uate it.... Sure enough: 3

Of course, you can *name* the program, too—to save for later....

Do It: [DROP] the EVAL result, and then ['][α][E][α][X][1][STO].... Just like any other freshly-named object, the program, now called EX1, will appear on the left side of your growing VAR menu.

---

*You'll notice, however, that the program can delay the execution of +, whereas you can't at the normal Command Line. To mimic the program even more closely, you can activate program entry mode without using [←][« »], by pressing [→][ENTRY].

But this E#1 program doesn't do anything particularly valuable (you already know what 1+2 is). So you ought to change it.

OK: Suppose you want E#1 to add 1 to *whatever* object is at Stack Level 1.

How?   You can't decompose a postfix program into its elements with **OBJ→**. In fact, the only way to change it (other than PURGE it and start over) is to edit it: ['] **E#1** (ENTER)(←)(EDIT). Now delete the 2: **SKIP→ SKIP→ DEL→**; and restore the program: (ENTER). Now E#1 will simply put the number 1 onto the Stack and then perform a **+**.

Try It: (←)(CLEAR), then (1) **E#1** gives a result of 2; **E#1** again: 3
(←)(())(3)(2)(SPC)(4)(4) **E#1** gives (33, 44).
(PRG) **TYPE** (2) **→LIST** (VAR) **E#1** gives { 3 (33, 44) 1 }.
(→)("")(α)(H)(α)(←)(I) **E#1** gives "Hi1".
['] (α)(H)(α)(←)(I)(ENTER) **E#1** gives 'Hi+1'.
(←)([ ])(1)(SPC)(2)(SPC)(3) **E#1** gives *an error* (you cannot add a scalar to a vector). This leaves the Stack *as it was at the time of the error* (the 1 put there by the program remains).

Don't worry—you'll get lots more sophisticated practice with programs (and most of the other objects later). The point here is this: Using a program—such as **E#1**—from your VAR menu is really *no different from using any built-in command*—such as (x²). Naming a program creates a new tool in your workshop, and it works like any built-in tool.

Directories

A directory—any directory (a phone book, a map, a kiosk in the mall, whatever)—is a reference tool to help you find what you need from among a given selection. And there are different directories for different selections. For example, it would be a hopeless mess to try to list all the telephone numbers in the country in one huge phone book, so the listings are broken down into different books. And each book is often divided even further—by city or suburb—into *subdirectories*.

The point is, a directory's very purpose is this dividing/subdividing effect. It offers you *only* a certain selection among "all possible items"—in order to simplify and narrow the field of your search (assuming, of course, that the selection uses some logical criterion—all the names in the phone book from the same city, etc.).

In the 48, you use directories in just that way: Your VAR menu—your toolbox for your own custom-built objects—is quite roomy, and you can put anything you want into it. You can divide it up into drawers, each with some more specific criterion for the named objects it contains. And you can even subdivide those drawers into still smaller compartments, then subcompartments, etc.

How does the 48 represent directories?

Directories are objects—just as arrays, strings and lists are objects—but because it's seldom useful to put a directory on your Stack workbench, there's no 48 delimiter reserved to denote a directory object. The best way to *see* one is to *build* one....

How do you build a directory?

To create a directory, just put a unique *name* into Level 1 of the Stack and invoke the CRDIR command....

Watch: Press ◁(CLEAR)(')(α)(α)(D)(I)(R)(1)(α)◁(MEMORY) ▮DIR▮ ▮CRDIR▮. (VAR).... The new name, ▮DIR1▮, is now in the VAR menu.

Notice the "file folder tab" on the top of the ▮DIR1▮ menu box. This is to help you distinguish directories from the other named objects.

How do you use a directory?

So you now have a new, empty directory called DIR1.

Question: Can you look into it—and store objects into it now?

Answer: Sure—but you need to *open* it first. Just *evaluate its name*—press ▮DIR1▮. Your VAR menu becomes *empty*, because now it's showing you only the contents of the DIR1 directory. And the Status Area shows a list, telling you "where" you are: **{ HOME DIR1 }**
That is, you started in your **HOME** "toolbox," then opened the **DIR1** "drawer" within that toolbox.

Now, to put something into this drawer, you do exactly what you always do—just STOre into a name.

Like So: For example, 1 ' αA STO puts the named object 'A' into your opened DIR1 drawer. With this drawer open, whenever you evaluate, store or recall 'A', you'll be referring to this 'A'.

Question: Does this replace the 'A' in your HOME directory—the one that contained the value of 4 (recall pages 118-123)?

Find Out: Return to the HOME directory (i.e. *close* the DIR1 drawer), by pressing →HOME.... The list in the Status Area now shows ⟨ HOME ⟩, and the VAR menu should look familiar. All right, *now* evaluate the name 'A' (press NXT ▮ A ▮ *). You get 4. So the 'A' in DIR1 is *different* than the 'A' in the HOME directory—like two **John Smith**'s in two different phone books. *You can use identical names for different objects if they're in different directories.*

When evaluating a name, apparently, the 48 looks for that name only in the *current* directory (HOME, in this case). Test that theory: Go back to DIR1 (NXT ▮DIR1▮) and evaluate 'A' (press ▮ A ▮).... Yep—you get 1—the value of the 'A' stored in the DIR1 directory.

---

*Remember that there are two items that look like ▮ A ▮—the one farther to the left is for 'a'; the other is for 'A' (but if you forget which is which, pressing ' ▮ A ▮ would tell you).

But: PURGe the name `'A'` from the DIR1 directory:
⟦'⟧ ⟦ A ⟧ ⟦←⟧⟦PURG⟧.

Now evaluate `'A'`: ⟦α⟧⟦A⟧⟦ENTER⟧.... You get 4 !

How can this be? The name `'A'` *doesn't exist* in DIR1—you just PURGed it. This is the value of the name `'A'` *in the HOME directory*—and yet you obtained it by evaluating `'A'` from the DIR1 directory!

This is because the `'A'` in HOME is *in your current PATH.*

As you've read, the directories you create in the HOME directory are "drawers"—subdivisions of that HOME directory "toolbox." And directories you create from any such "drawer" are further subdivisions ("compartments") *within that drawer.* So, starting from HOME, to get to any particular directory, you sequentially open the correct drawer, the correct compartment within that drawer, etc. That is, you traverse an access PATH through your directory structure.

That list in the Status Area is your PATH list—the description of the PATH you took from HOME to get to where you are now. When you evaluate or recall a name, the 48 first looks in the *current* directory (the directory at the *end* of the PATH list). But if it can't find the specified name there, the 48 will methodically search *backward* through that PATH list until it either finds the name or exhausts all directories in that PATH list.

A little terminology clarification: Directories within other directories are commonly called *subdirectories*. So DIR1 is a subdirectory of HOME and HOME is the *parent* directory of DIR1.

A directory may contain many objects—and many subdirectories.

Watch: Create a subdirectory, `'DIR2'`, in the HOME directory.

Like So: →[HOME] ['] **DIR1** [←] [2] [←][MEMORY] **DIR** **CRDIR** [VAR].... Now DIR2 is DIR1's "sibling"—another drawer in the HOME toolbox.

Next, create another directory, `'DIR3'`, *inside* DIR2: First, open the empty DIR2 (press **DIR2**). Then: ['] [α][α][D][I][R][3] [α][←][MEMORY] **DIR** **CRDIR** [VAR].

You now have a directory (DIR3) within a directory (DIR2) within a directory (HOME). So HOME is DIR3's "grandparent," if you will. Since a family tree is such an obvious analogy for this directory structure, it is commonly referred to as a directory *tree*.

Practice moving through the tree:

Store 2 into `'D'` in DIR3: **DIR3** [2] ['][α][D] [STO].

Store 8 into `'C'` in DIR2: [←][UP] [8] ['][α][C] [STO]. The UP(DIR) command moves you up to the current directory's *parent*.

Store 16 into `'B'` in DIR1: [←][UP] **DIR1** [1][6] ['][α][B] [STO].

Questions: From which directories can you now recall and evaluate 'A', 'B', 'C', and 'D'? Feel free to use your 48 to help.

Answers: 'A': HOME, DIR1, DIR2, DIR3
'B': DIR1
'C': DIR2, DIR3
'D': DIR3

Remember: You can recall or evaluate any name in the current directory's PATH. Since *all* PATHs contain the HOME directory, anything stored there is accessible from *any* subdirectory—no matter how many generations removed. By contrast, objects stored in the "leaves" of the tree (i.e. in directories with no children) are accessible *only* from that "leaf" directory.

Now: Time to clean up: There are two ways to PURGE a directory....

As with any other name, you may use the PURGE command on a directory name—but *only* if that directory is *empty* (so you can't easily destroy a lot of valuable information with PURGE).

Or, if you're *sure* that you want to destroy a directory *and* everything in it (objects, subdirectories, their contents—the whole shootin' match), use PGDIR (PurGe DIRectory). PGDIR assumes that you know what you're doing. It removes a directory *and its contents*—so use it with caution (go ahead and do this now): →HOME ' DIR1 ENTER ' DIR2 ← MEMORY DIR PGDIR PGDIR VAR.

Objects: A Summary

No sense kidding yourself: You've covered a lot in this long chapter. You've seen how to build and at least begin to use these basic object types in the 48:

Real numbers	Units	Lists
Complex numbers	Vectors	Arrays
Flags	Binary integers	
Strings	Tags	
Names	Algebraic objects	
Postfix programs	Directories	

Yes, there are few other object types that you haven't seen yet—mainly because they're for special purposes—plotting, programming, backing up your data, etc.

Right now, hold your place here and look back at pages 14-15—"The Big Picture".... Surely the keyboard's organizational structure ought to seem more familiar now. And of course, the Stack is definitely "home turf" by now, right? But even that example directory tree structure on page 15 ought to be clearer, now that you know a little about sub-directories, parent directories and PATHs, no?

But just in case, here are a few more exercises to help you put it all together. These quiz problems will force you to *use and combine* what you know—and you'll even see a few new variations and features not covered before now—so heads up!—and enjoy....

Test Your Objectivity

1. Sum the first 10 positive integers. Now sum the first 1000 positive integers.

2. Silver (Ag) crystallizes in a face-centered cubic unit cell (4 atoms). The density of Ag is 10.5 g/cm^3. The atomic mass of silver is 107.868 g/mol. There are 6.022×10^{23} atoms/mole. Find the mass, volume and dimensions (in Ångstroms) of a silver unit cell.

3. In an elementary chemical reaction, $e^{\frac{-E_A}{RT}}$ is the fraction of collisions with enough energy to react. E_A is the activation energy; R is the ideal gas constant (8.314 J/K-mol); T is the absolute temperature (in Kelvins). Find the fraction of successful collisions for a reaction at 980° F with an activation energy of 2.14×10^4 J/mol.

4. What are the differences between { 1 2 3 4 } and [1 2 3 4]? How would you convert between them?

5. You can add elements to a list using the ⊕ key, but how might you *delete*, say, the last element? The first element?

6. How would you change the value 1+2i into 2+i on the 48?

7. Fill in the table below to compare the costs and benefits of three strategies for replacing part of the current U.S. daily use of petroleum—now totalling about 15 million barrels:

Option	Costs (Savings)	Energy gain (bbl/d)	% of current use
80 nuclear reactors	Total: $_____	_____	____%
80 coal plants	Total: $_____	_____	____%
Simple efficiency measures	H$_2$O heat: _____	_____	____%
	Appliances:_____	_____	____%
	Lighting: _____	_____	____%
	Tire infl.: _____	_____	____%
	Total: $_____	_____	____%

Nuclear reactor (1000 MW):
Capital invest. (3-5-yr constr./testing): $ 1200/kW
Fuel and maintenance (for 25-year life): 200/kW
Disposal/cleanup (100-1,000 years): 50000/kW

Coal-fired plant (1000 MW):
Capital invest. (3-year constr./testing): $ 1000/kW
Fuel and maintenance (for 50-year life): 100/kW
Disposal/cleanup (10 years): 10000/kW

Efficiencies: 100 million U.S. households each use the energy equivalent average of 1253 gallons of oil per year—at a cost of about $1,200. 40% of this goes for space heating, 20% for water heating, 15% for major appliances, 10% for lighting, the rest for other uses. 140 million U.S. cars average 10,000 miles per year each, at 19 mpg. 1 barrel of oil has 5900 MJ of chemical energy and produces 16.4 gallons of gasoline. A unit of electrical energy requires 3 units of oil energy. Electric plants typically operate at 75% of rated capacity.

Low-flow heads on faucets and showers cost $40 per household and last at least 10 years. That plus using cold water rinse in the washer would save 20% on water heating. Lowering the H$_2$O heater to 130°F. and raising the freezer and refrigerator to 0° and 40° F. would save at least 5% on appliance usage. Using compact fluorescent light bulbs (20 per household) would cost $150 more to buy (for the same 5-yr. life) as incandescent bulbs but save 75% in electricity. Inflating car tires to correct pressures would save 3% in fuel consumption.

8. What's $\sin^{-1}(2)$? What are the units of the solution angle? What does this solution mean?

9. Find the angle, ϕ, between $-9\mathbf{i}+4\mathbf{j}-2\mathbf{k}$ and $(12, 1.39\,\text{rad}, 0.48\,\text{rad})$.

10. Find the volume of the parallelepiped defined by:

$$a = 3\mathbf{i} + 3\mathbf{j} + 5\mathbf{k} \qquad b = 7\mathbf{i} + \mathbf{j} - .2\mathbf{k} \qquad c = \mathbf{i} + 8\mathbf{j} - \mathbf{k}$$

11. If $A = (1,2,3)$, $B = (-3\angle 25°, -.2)$, and $C = (\tfrac{1}{3}\angle \sqrt{2}\,\text{rad}, -6\,\text{rad})$, find the unit vector that points in the same direction as of the *sum* of the real and imaginary portions of $14.5A - 0.2B + (1+i)C$

12. Within the vector $[\ 2\ 4\ 6\ 8\ 10\ ]$, how could you change the 8 to 19? How could you change the 2 to $(1, 1)$?

13. Create the vector $[\ 1\ 2\ ]$. Now redimension it to a 5-element vector. Then change the third element to 5. Then "dot" it with $[\ 5\ 4\ 3\ 2\ 1\ ]$.

Sources:

The 1990 Information Please Almanac, Houghton Mifflin Company, Boston, 1990.

50 Simple Things You Can Do To Save The Earth, The Earth Works Group, Earthworks Press, Berkeley, 1989 (book available through: NRDC, 40 West 20th St., New York, NY 10011).

Ecoscience: Population, Resources, Environment, Erlich, Erlich and Holdren, W.H. Freeman & Co., San Francisco, 1977.

14. Convert the vector [1 2 3 4 5 6 7 8 9] into a **3 x 3** array. Then change element$_{12}$ to **10**. Then convert the resulting array into an array with complex elements.

15. How might you extract individual rows from the result of problem **14**? Would these be vectors?

16. Legends still speak of that dark and fateful night, over a century ago, when a U.S. Mail Express locomotive became a runaway and collided with a long-haul Canadian grain engine at a remote prairie border junction. The crews may have bailed out in time, but they were never found. Your theory: The collision startled a large herd of bison nearby, whose ensuing stampede obliterated the entire scene. You've surmised that the wreckage itself landed somewhere out in a bison mud wallow, sinking well out of sight beneath the muck and chaos of the stampede. Vague stories of some such incident—pieced together from railroad memorabilia in both countries—have allowed you to estimate these speeds, compass headings and weights for each engine (including its coal tender) at the point of collision:

Engine	Speed	Heading	Weight
Squash Blossom Special	88 mph	44°19'	150 tons
Home, Wheat, Home	110 km/hr	256°32'	300,000 kg

Problem: Which government should have excavation jurisdiction over your proposed International Peace-Railroad Memorial Mud Wallow?

17. Find the total hours worked by each person and by all together:

	Andy	Beth	Carla	David
Mon.	8	8	5	7
Tues.	8	8	6	7
Wed.	4	7	5	7
Thurs.	8	7	4	8
Fri.	8	8	5	7

18. Test matrix multiplication commutativity with these:

$$A = \begin{bmatrix} 1 & 2 \\ 3 & 4 \end{bmatrix} \quad \text{and} \quad B = \begin{bmatrix} 16 & 9 \\ 4 & 1 \end{bmatrix}$$

19. Use ÷42 to help you build *complex numbers*.

20. Set ENG display notation and polar/cylindrical vector mode—using only one page of one menu and the digit keys.

21. Find the 48's current binary wordsize without using RCWS.

22. What's the easiest way to *preserve* the system settings—such as those discussed in problems **19-21**—for quick restoration later?

23. Calculate $2_{10} \times (\text{FFF}_{16} \div 2_{10})$ in 16-bit integers.

24. Key in # 100d and duplicate it. Then convert one copy to a string. Then set binary mode....Why are the two results different?

25. Change "You understand?" to "You understand!"

26. Build the string "Vol.= 4.0 gal." without using the ④ key. Then, starting with such a string, extract the numeric value.

27. Format a number in scientific notation—such as 6.022E23— within a string, in this format: "6.022 * 10^(23)" What will OBJ→ produce from this string?

28. Use PURGe to rename 'A' as 'x'. Then use this name to tag the solution to $x = \dfrac{-b \pm \sqrt{b^2 - 4ac}}{2a}$, for $a = 1$, $b = -8$, and $c = 15$.

29. Set flag –3 and try to build the solution to prob. **28** "from scratch."

30. Key in the names 'π', 'i' and 'e' and evaluate them. Now set flag –2 and repeat this exercise.

31. How can you PURGe more than one name at a time?

32. Evaluate the expression $'2*x+y'$ for:

    a. $x = -2y$ **c.** $x = t, \ y = t - 1$

    b. $y = -2x$ **d.** $x = z - 3y, \quad y = y - 3z$

33. Write the solutions to problem **4** as two complementary programs, named L→V and V→L. Test them with these lists:

```
{ 0 }                      { 1 2 3 }
{ 1 0 (1,0) }              { }
```


34. Use L→V and/or V→L to write another program, called LABS ("List
ABSolute value"), that produces a 1-element list containing the
"magnitude" (the "square root of the sum of the squares") of the
argument list. Test LABS with these lists:

    a.   `{ 1 2 3 4 }`
    b.   `{ (1,1) (-3,4) }`
    c.   `{ [ 1 2 ] [ 3 4 ] }`

35. When would evaluating a directory's name *not* send you to that
directory? How could you give a directory two different names?

36. Suppose you want to build yourself a little phone book: Write a
program that will open the correct one among 26 alphabetically
named (A through Z) subdirectories—depending upon the first
letter of the string you key in.

Objective Answers

1. Just a reminder of the options you have for keying in objects and doing arithmetic with them on the Stack. For example:

   [1][ENTER][2][+][3][+][4][+][5][+][6][+][7][+][8][+][9][+][1][0][+], *or*

   [1][SPC][2][SPC][3][SPC][4][SPC][5][SPC][6][SPC][7][SPC][8][SPC][9][SPC][1][0]
   [+][+][+][+][+][+][+][+][+] , etc.   Answer: 55

   Of course, no such method is good for adding a *thousand* numbers, but observe that

   $$1+2+3\ldots +998+999+1000$$
   $$=(1+1000)+(2+999)+(3+998)\ldots+(500+501)$$
   $$= 1001\times500.$$

   So: [1][0][0][1][ENTER][5][0][0][×]   Answer: 500500

2. [←][MODES] **FMT** [2] **SCI**. Key in the atomic mass: [1][0][7][·][8][6][8] [→][UNITS] **MASS** **G** [NXT][NXT][→] **MOL**. Next, key in Avogadro's number: [6][·][0][2][2][EEX][2][3][→] **MOL**. Note that the item being counted (atoms) is implied—as with cycles in "cycles per second" (Hz) or any other discrete item. Now divide the two arguments: [÷] (that's grams per atom), then multiply by 4 (atoms per cell): [4][×].... Result: 7.16E-22_g   (grams per cell)

   Volume is mass divided by density. You have the mass already, so key in the density: [1][0][·][5][NXT] **G** [→][UNITS] **VOL** [→] **CM^3**. And divide: [÷]   Result: 6.82E-23_cm^3

   And, since the unit cell is a cube, just take the cube root of the volume to find the length of an edge: [3][→][x√y]. Now just convert to Å: [→][UNITS] **LENG** [←][PREV][←] **Å** .... Result: 4.09E0_Å

3. 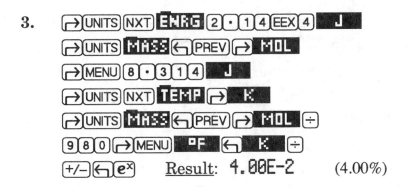 ⇨UNITS ⟨NXT⟩ **ENRG** 2 · 1 4 ⟨EEX⟩ 4 **J**
⇨UNITS **MASS** ⟨PREV⟩ ⇨ **MOL**
⇨MENU 8 · 3 1 4 **J**
⇨UNITS ⟨NXT⟩ **TEMP** ⇨ **K**
⇨UNITS **MASS** ⟨PREV⟩ ⇨ **MOL** ÷
9 8 0 ⇨MENU **°F** ⟨ **K** ÷
⟨+/−⟩ ⟨e^x⟩   <u>Result</u>: 4.00E-2   (4.00%)

4. One is a list; the other is a vector.

To convert, start with the list: ⟨MODES⟩ **FMT STD**
⟨{} 1 ⟨SPC⟩ 2 ⟨SPC⟩ 3 ⟨SPC⟩ 4 ⟨ENTER⟩ (and ⟨PRG⟩ **TYPE**).

Then **OBJ→ →ARR** is the easiest conversion; **OBJ→** leaves the
Stack all ready for **→ARR**.

To convert back: **OBJ→ OBJ→** ⟨◄⟩ **→LIST**. Since **→LIST** needs a
real number for a length argument, you use **OBJ→** ⟨◄⟩ to *extract*
that real number from the *list*-type length argument produced by
decomposing the vector.

5. Use the list from problem **4**: **OBJ→** 1 − **→LIST** deletes the first
element; **OBJ→** ⟨SWAP⟩⟨DROP⟩ 1 − **→LIST** deletes the last element.

6. Start with 1+2*i*: ⟨()⟩ 1 ⟨SPC⟩ 2 ⟨ENTER⟩ (and ⟨NXT⟩ to go to the second
page of the TYPE menu). Then **C→R** ⟨SWAP⟩ **R→C** does the job.

7. Do the **power plants** first: Calculate the barrels of oil saved by typical daily generating levels: ⟵MODES **FMT** ⟨1⟩ **ENG** (to reflect the certainties of the data). Then ⟨1⟩⟨0⟩⟨0⟩⟨0⟩↱_⟨α⟩⟨M⟩⟨α⟩⟨W⟩ ⟨ENTER⟩⟨7⟩⟨5⟩⟨MTH⟩ **REAL** ⁝ ⟨1⟩↱_⟨α⟩⟵⟨D⟩⟨ENTER⟩⟨×⟩⟨3⟩⟨×⟩⟨0⟩↱_ ⟨α⟩⟨M⟩⟨α⟩⟨J⟩⟨ENTER⟩⟨+⟩⟨5⟩⟨9⟩⟨0⟩⟨0⟩↱_⟨α⟩⟨M⟩⟨α⟩⟨J⟩⟨ENTER⟩⟨÷⟩⟨8⟩⟨0⟩⟨×⟩ (note the unit *prefixes* here). <u>Result</u>: **2.6E6** The oil (barrels) that eighty 1000-MW power plants would save daily. The costs?...

⟨1⟩⟨0⟩⟨0⟩⟨0⟩⟨EEX⟩⟨6⟩⟨ENTER⟩⟨EEX⟩⟨3⟩⟨÷⟩⟨8⟩⟨0⟩⟨×⟩⟨ENTER⟩ (rated kW for 80 plants)
⟨1⟩⟨2⟩⟨0⟩⟨0⟩⟨ENTER⟩⟨2⟩⟨0⟩⟨0⟩⟨+⟩⟨5⟩⟨0⟩⟨0⟩⟨0⟩⟨0⟩⟨+⟩⟨×⟩⟨2⟩⟨5⟩⟨÷⟩⟨3⟩⟨6⟩⟨5⟩⟨÷⟩
<u>Result</u>: **450.E6** That's $450 million spent per *day* for 25 years for the 80 nuclear plants

⟵⟨1⟩⟨0⟩⟨0⟩⟨0⟩⟨ENTER⟩⟨1⟩⟨0⟩⟨0⟩⟨+⟩⟨1⟩⟨0⟩⟨0⟩⟨0⟩⟨0⟩⟨+⟩⟨×⟩⟨5⟩⟨0⟩⟨÷⟩⟨3⟩⟨6⟩⟨5⟩⟨÷⟩
<u>Result</u>: **49.E6** That's $49 million spent per *day* for 50 years for the 80 coal-fired plants

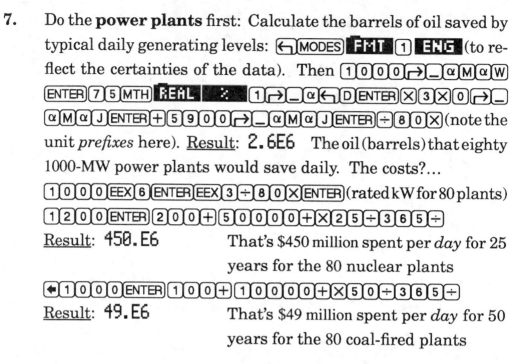

The **efficiencies**. First, the daily oil savings in water heating:
⟨1⟩⟨2⟩⟨5⟩⟨3⟩⟨ENTER⟩⟨3⟩⟨6⟩⟨5⟩⟨÷⟩⟨·⟩⟨2⟩⟨×⟩⟨·⟩⟨2⟩⟨×⟩⟨EEX⟩⟨8⟩⟨×⟩↱⟨UNITS⟩ **VOL** ⟨NXT⟩
GAL ⟨NXT⟩⟨NXT⟩⟵ **BBL** <u>Result</u>: **330.E3_bbl**
The $avings: ⟨4⟩⟨0⟩⟨+/−⟩⟨ENTER⟩⟨1⟩⟨0⟩⟨÷⟩ (the plumbing ought to last at least 10 years) ⟨1⟩⟨2⟩⟨0⟩⟨0⟩⟨ENTER⟩⟨·⟩⟨2⟩⟨×⟩⟨·⟩⟨2⟩⟨×⟩⟨+⟩⟨3⟩⟨6⟩⟨5⟩⟨÷⟩⟨EEX⟩⟨8⟩⟨×⟩
<u>Result</u>: **12.E6** That's $12 million saved per day.

Next, the daily oil savings in electrical appliance efficiency:
⟨1⟩⟨2⟩⟨5⟩⟨3⟩⟨ENTER⟩⟨3⟩⟨6⟩⟨5⟩⟨÷⟩⟨·⟩⟨1⟩⟨5⟩⟨×⟩⟨·⟩⟨0⟩⟨5⟩⟨×⟩⟨EEX⟩⟨8⟩⟨×⟩⟨NXT⟩⟨NXT⟩
GAL ⟨NXT⟩⟨NXT⟩⟵ **BBL** ⟨3⟩⟨×⟩ <u>Result</u>: **180.E3_bbl**
The $avings: ⟨1⟩⟨2⟩⟨0⟩⟨0⟩⟨ENTER⟩⟨3⟩⟨6⟩⟨5⟩⟨÷⟩⟨·⟩⟨1⟩⟨5⟩⟨×⟩⟨·⟩⟨0⟩⟨5⟩⟨×⟩⟨EEX⟩⟨8⟩⟨×⟩
<u>Result</u>: **2.5E6** That's $2.5 million saved per day.

Then there's the daily oil savings in electrical lighting efficiency:
⟨1⟩⟨2⟩⟨5⟩⟨3⟩⟨ENTER⟩⟨3⟩⟨6⟩⟨5⟩⟨÷⟩⟨·⟩⟨1⟩⟨×⟩⟨·⟩⟨7⟩⟨5⟩⟨×⟩⟨EEX⟩⟨8⟩⟨×⟩⟨NXT⟩⟨NXT⟩ **GAL**
⟨NXT⟩⟨NXT⟩⟵ **BBL** ⟨3⟩⟨×⟩ <u>Result</u>: **1.8E6_bbl**

The $avings: ⎡1⎤⎡5⎤⎡0⎤⎡+/−⎤⎡ENTER⎤⎡5⎤⎡÷⎤⎡1⎤⎡2⎤⎡0⎤⎡0⎤⎡ENTER⎤⎡.⎤⎡1⎤⎡X⎤⎡.⎤⎡7⎤⎡5⎤
⎡X⎤⎡+⎤⎡3⎤⎡6⎤⎡5⎤⎡÷⎤⎡EEX⎤⎡8⎤⎡X⎤
Result: **16.E6**   That's $16 million saved per day.

Finally, the daily oil savings from proper tire inflation:
⎡1⎤⎡0⎤⎡0⎤⎡0⎤⎡0⎤⎡ENTER⎤⎡1⎤⎡9⎤⎡÷⎤⎡1⎤⎡4⎤⎡0⎤⎡EEX⎤⎡6⎤⎡X⎤⎡.⎤⎡0⎤⎡3⎤⎡X⎤⎡3⎤⎡6⎤⎡5⎤⎡÷⎤⎡ENTER⎤
⎡1⎤⎡6⎤⎡.⎤⎡4⎤⎡÷⎤   Result: **370.E3**
The $avings: ⎡←⎤⎡1⎤⎡.⎤⎡2⎤⎡5⎤⎡X⎤ (cheap for a gallon of gas by now)
        Result: **7.6E6** $7.6 million saved per day.

So here's the filled-in table (remember—these are *daily* figures):

Option	$Costs (Savings)		Energy gain (bbl/d)	% of current use
80 nuclear reactors	**Total:**	**$ 450 million**	**2.6 million**	17%
80 coal plants	**Total:**	**$ 49 million**	**2.6 million**	17%
Efficiency measures	H₂O heat:	($12 million)	0.33 million	2.2%
	Appls.:	(2.5 million)	0.18 million	1.2%
	Lighting:	(16 million)	1.8 million	12%
	Tire infl.:	(7.6 million)	0.37 million	2.5%
	Total:	**($39.1 million)**	**2.7 million**	**18%**

So, to add 17-18% to the nation's daily oil supply—without any change to your life-style—which would you rather do:

spend $50-450 million/day—and wait 3-5 years for results?
or save $40 million/day—with immediate results?

8. Press ⟨2⟩⟨←⟩⟨ASIN⟩. <u>Answer</u>: (1.57079632679, -1.31695789692) (assumes RECT and STD modes here). A complex trig argument doesn't carry the circular geometric interpretation ("units") that real arguments do. The general sine function is an infinite series

sum: $\sin x = x - \dfrac{x^3}{3!} + \dfrac{x^5}{5!} - \dfrac{x^7}{7!} + \cdots$

9. The angle, ϕ, between any two vectors, A and B, is given by

$$\phi = \cos^{-1}\left(\frac{\mathbf{A} \cdot \mathbf{B}}{|\mathbf{A}||\mathbf{B}|}\right)$$

Be sure that you enter each vector in its proper mode:

⟨←⟩⟨[ ]⟩⟨9⟩⟨+/−⟩⟨SPC⟩⟨4⟩⟨SPC⟩⟨2⟩⟨+/−⟩⟨ENTER⟩⟨'⟩⟨α⟩⟨A⟩⟨STO⟩;
⟨MTH⟩ **VECTR** ⟨NXT⟩ **SPHER** ⟨←⟩⟨RAD⟩⟨1⟩⟨2⟩⟨SPC⟩⟨1⟩⟨·⟩⟨3⟩⟨9⟩⟨SPC⟩⟨·⟩⟨4⟩⟨8⟩⟨NXT⟩
→V3 ⟨'⟩⟨α⟩⟨B⟩⟨STO⟩. Now calculate: ⟨VAR⟩ **A** ⟨NXT⟩ **B** ⟨→⟩⟨MENU⟩
DOT ⟨VAR⟩ **A** ⟨→⟩⟨MENU⟩ **ABS** ⟨÷⟩⟨VAR⟩⟨NXT⟩ **B**
⟨→⟩⟨MENU⟩ **ABS** ⟨÷⟩⟨←⟩⟨ACOS⟩....<u>Result</u>: 1.64093275493 (rad)

10. The volume of a parallelepiped is the absolute value of its vectors' *triple scalar product*, defined as any of these variations:

a • (b x c)	**b • (a x c)**	**c • (a x b)**
a • (c x b)	**b • (c x a)**	**c • (b x a)**

So: ⟨←⟩⟨[ ]⟩⟨7⟩⟨SPC⟩⟨1⟩⟨SPC⟩⟨·⟩⟨2⟩⟨+/−⟩⟨ENTER⟩⟨←⟩⟨[ ]⟩⟨1⟩⟨SPC⟩⟨8⟩⟨SPC⟩⟨1⟩⟨+/−⟩
⟨ENTER⟩⟨←⟩⟨[ ]⟩⟨3⟩⟨SPC⟩⟨3⟩⟨SPC⟩⟨5⟩⟨ENTER⟩. Then evaluate the function:
⟨MTH⟩ **VECTR** **CROSS** **DOT** 　　 <u>Result</u>: 297.2

11. Build and name your three vectors: ⟵ MODES **ANGL**, then
RECT ⟵ [ ] 1 SPC 2 SPC 3 ENTER ' α A STO
CYLIN DEG ⟵ [ ] 3 +/− ⟶ ∠ 2 5 SPC · 2 +/− ENTER ' α B STO
SPHER RAD 3 1/x 2 √x 6 +/− MTH **VECTR →V3** ' α C STO
Then: VAR NXT 1 4 · 5 **A** × · 2 **B** × − ⟵ PREV ⟵ ( )
1 SPC 1 **C** × + ⟵ MODES **ANGL RECT** —to see the real and
imaginary portions of the complex vector result.

Next, PRG **TYPE** NXT **C→R** (yes, **C→R** / **R→C** will split/build
complex-valued *vectors*, too).

Then + adds the two real-valued vectors, and to find the corresponding *unit* vector, you divide the vector by its own magnitude:
MTH **VECTR** ENTER **ABS** ÷ ....   Answer:

[.273121183844 .533411568534 .80054788582]

12. First, build the vector: 2 SPC 4 SPC 6 SPC 8 SPC 1 0 SPC 5 PRG
TYPE →ARR. Now 4 SPC 1 9 SPC α α P U T ENTER. The first
argument for PUT is the *position* of the target element in the vector (or array or list). The second argument is its new value.
Of course, you can't put a complex value into a real-valued vector,
so ⟵ ( ) 1 SPC 0 × first, to convert the vector, then 1 SPC ⟵ ( )
1 SPC 1 ENTER α α P U T ENTER does the job.

13. Press ⟵ [ ] 1 SPC 2 ENTER, then ⟵ { } 5 ENTER MTH **MATR MAKE**
RDM. The ReDiMension command needs a list argument to tell
it the new dimension of your vector (for an array, you would need
two dimension numbers in this argument). Then 3 SPC 5 SPC
α α P U T ENTER changes the third element, and ⟵ [ ] 5 SPC
4 SPC 3 SPC 2 SPC 1 MTH **VECTR DOT** finds the Answer: 28

14. Build the vector: `←` `[ ]` `1` `SPC` `2` `SPC` `3` `SPC` `4` `SPC` `5` `SPC` `6` `SPC` `7` `SPC` `8` `SPC` `9` `ENTER`. Then `←` `{ }` `3` `SPC` `3` `ENTER` `MTH` **MATR** **MAKE** **RDM** redimensions; `←` `{ }` `1` `SPC` `2` `ENTER` `1` `0` `ENTER` `α` `α` `P` `U` `T` `ENTER` to change element$_{12}$. `←` `( )` `1` `SPC` `0` `×` makes it complex.

15. Simply *multiply* by the appropriate *row identity* matrices. For example, to extract the first row, multiply by `[[ 1 0 0 ]]` (`←` `[ ]` `←` `[ ]` `1` `SPC` `0` `SPC` `0` `←` `SWAP` `×`). And for the second row, multiply by `[[ 0 1 0 ]]`, and so on. *Notice* that the order of your multiplication is important. Notice, too, that each result is an *array* (**1x3**), not a vector.

16. This is just a vector problem—with *momentum* (mass × velocity): `→` `POLAR` `←` `RAD` (you want polar mode, angles in degrees), then `←` `MODES` **FMT** `1` **FIX** `1` `5` `0` `→` `_` `α` `α` `←` `α` `T` `O` `N` `ENTER` `8` `8` `→` `_` `α` `α` `←` `α` `M` `P` `H` `ENTER` `×` `←` `UNITS` **UBASE** **UVAL** `4` `4` `•` `1` `9` `←` `TIME` `NXT` **HMS→** `MTH` **VECTR** **→V2** .

(UBASE, UVAL and HMS→ are new here; notice how they work.)

That's the first train. The second train: `3` `EEX` `5` `→` `_` `α` `←` `K` `α` `←` `G` `ENTER` `1` `1` `0` `→` `_` `α` `α` `←` `α` `K` `P` `H` `α` `ENTER` `×` `←` `UNITS` **UBASE** **UVAL** `2` `5` `6` `•` `3` `2` `→` `MENU` **HMS→** `MTH` **VECTR** **→V2** .

Now, the big moment: `+` Result: `[ 5445411.1 ∢-71.9 ]`

But compass bearings proceed *clockwise from north* (not counterclockwise from "east," as in math conventions). The momentum heading of the wreckage (–71.9°) therefore indicates *north* of due west (–90°)—so it looks like Canada should hire the backhoe.

17. One possible strategy: Build a "five-day" vector for each person.

←[MODES] **FMT** **STO** ←[MODES] **ANGL** **RECT**

←[[ ]] 8 [SPC] 8 [SPC] 4 [SPC] 8 [SPC] 8 [ENTER] ' α A [STO]

←[[ ]] 8 [SPC] 8 [SPC] 7 [SPC] 7 [SPC] 8 [ENTER] ' α B [STO]

←[[ ]] 5 [SPC] 6 [SPC] 5 [SPC] 4 [SPC] 5 [ENTER] ' α C [STO]

←[[ ]] 7 [SPC] 7 [SPC] 7 [SPC] 8 [SPC] 7 [ENTER] ' α D [STO]

Now press [MTH] **MATR** **NORM**, and use **CNRM** on each person's vector to sum his/her hours (α A **CNRM**, α B **CNRM**, etc.). Then you can either sum these results (+ + +)—*or* sum the vectors (α A [ENTER] α B + ...) and **CNRM**—to total all hours: 135

18. ←[[ ]] ←[[ ]] 1 [SPC] 2 ▶ 3 [SPC] 4 [ENTER] ' α A [STO], and
←[[ ]] ←[[ ]] 1 6 [SPC] 9 ▶ 4 [SPC] 1 [ENTER] ' α B [STO].

Then [VAR][NXT] **A** **B** [×] and **B** **A** [×].... So matrix multiplication is *not* commutative.

19. To use **→V2** to build complex numbers, just set system flag –19: 1 9 +/− [SPC] α S α F [ENTER]. Now 1 [ENTER] 2 [MTH] **VECTR** **→V2**. Your result is a complex number, right?

20. Use system flags. When flag –15 is *clear* (press 1 5 +/− ←[MODES] **FLAG** **CF**), and flag –16 is *set* (1 6 +/− **SF**), this activates polar/cylindrical mode. Similarly, the combination of 4 9 +/− **SF** and 5 0 +/− **SF** activates ENG mode. Clear all four of these flags before going on.

21. The 48's current binary wordsize is determined by the states of system flags –5 through –10. These six flags form their own six-bit binary integer whose value *plus 1* becomes the machine's wordsize (the wordsize ranges from 1 to 64; a six-bit binary word represents values from 0 to 63—hence the addition of 1).

To extract this number from the flag settings, test those six flags, line up the bits and read the value: [PRG] [TEST] [NXT][NXT], then

Key-strokes	[1][0][+/–] [F5?]	[9][+/–] [F5?]	[8][+/–] [F5?]	[7][+/–] [F5?]	[6][+/–] [F5?]	[5][+/–] [F5?]
Results:	0	0	0	1	1	1

Thus, the wordsize here is $000111_2 + 1$, or 8_{10}

Alternatively, you could do it with math: Start with the adjustment value, 1: [←][CLEAR][1][ENTER]. Then test each flag and multiply the result by that flag's *place value* in the six-bit integer:
[1][0][+/–] [F5?] [3][2][×][+][9][+/–] [F5?] [1][6][×][+]
[8][+/–] [F5?] [8][×][+][7][+/–] [F5?] [4][×][+][6][+/–] [F5?] [2][×][+]
[5][+/–] [F5?] [+]   Result: 8

22. The easiest way to *preserve* the 48's system settings is to save the binary integers that represent the values of all the flags:
[α][α][R][C][L][F][ENTER]['][α][α][S][Y][S][1][α][STO]
Now all flag states are saved as the VARiable SYS1. And since you can have all the VARiables you want, this means you can save *any number* of different flag settings—both the 48's system flags and your own user flags!

23. Press [MTH] **BASE** [NXT] [1][6] **STWS** [NXT] **HEX** [→][#][α][α][F][F][F]
[ENTER][2][÷][2][X]   Result: **# FFEh**
You *don't* get **# FFFh** back again, because binary division truncates any remainder: Since FFF_{16} is an odd number (4095_{10}), divid-
ing by 2 resulted in 2047_{10} (not 2047.5), and so multiplying by 2
then gave 4094_{10}, or FFE_{16}.

24. Press **DEC** [→][#][1][0][0][ENTER][ENTER], and then [PRG] **TYPE** **→STR**
[→][MENU] **BIN** .... The results differ because they're different objects. Only a binary integer object changes its displayed appearance in response to a change in the binary integer format. The
string was created with the *characters* it encountered in the format of the binary integer *at the moment* you pressed **→STR**.

25. First, press [→][""][α][α][Y][↩][α][O][U][SPC][U][N][D][E][R][S][T][A][N][D]
[↩][←][ENTER] (remember the many characters on the shifted keys
when in alpha mode—use your CHARS menu to help you). Then
[↩][EDIT] **SKIP→** **SKIP→** [◀][←][α][↩][DEL][ENTER].

26. [→][""][α][α][V][↩][α][O][L][·][↩][=][SPC][ENTER] [1][ENTER][α][α][F][I][X]
[ENTER][2][ENTER][ENTER][+] (gets **4.0** without the [4] key). Then
[+][→][""][SPC][α][α][↩][α][G][A][L][·][ENTER][+]. To *extract* the value, as-
sume you know only its surrounding characters in the string, and
use some handy string dissecting commands: [ENTER][ENTER]
[→][""][SPC][ENTER][α][α][P][O][S][ENTER][1][+][SWAP][α][α][S][I][Z][E][ENTER]
[α][α][S][U][B][ENTER][ENTER][→][""][SPC][ENTER][α][α][P][O][S][ENTER][1][−][1]
[↩][SWAP][α][α][S][U][B][ENTER][PRG] **TYPE** **OBJ→** .... Result: **4.0**

27. ⍺⍺⌷S⌷T⌷D⌷ENTER⌷6⌷·⌷0⌷2⌷2⌷EEX⌷2⌷3⌷ENTER⌷ENTER⌷MTH⌷**REAL**
⌷NXT⌷**MANT**⌷SWAP⌷**XPON**⌷→⌷"⌷"⌷←⌷(⌷)⌷←⌷+⌷→⌷"⌷"⌷⍺⍺⌷SPC⌷×⌷SPC⌷
⌷1⌷0⌷⍺⌷→⌷ENTRY⌷→⌷ENTRY⌷y^x⌷←⌷(⌷)⌷DEL⌷ENTER⌷SWAP⌷+⌷+⌷.
OBJ→ will produce an Invalid Syntax error, because it
tries to decompose a string into objects and put them onto the
Stack in *postfix* notation. So if you want a string that separates
the mantissa and exponent but still evaluates back to the number, you would need to use "6.022 10 23 ^ *".

28. Press VAR⌷NXT⌷ A ⌷ ' ⌷ A ⌷←⌷PURG⌷'⌷⍺⌷←⌷X⌷STO⌷1⌷←⌷PREV⌷
←⌷ A ⌷,⌷NXT⌷8⌷+/-⌷←⌷ B ⌷(the more recent B),⌷1⌷5⌷←⌷
C . Then⌷'⌷ EQ ⌷ENTER⌷←⌷EDIT⌷▶⌷▶⌷▶⌷▶⌷▶⌷◀⌷−⌷ENTER⌷ EQ ⌷
EVAL⌷←⌷PREV⌷'⌷ X ⌷PRG⌷**TYPE**⌷**→TAG**....   Result: x: 3

29. 3⌷+/-⌷SPC⌷⍺⌷S⌷⍺⌷F⌷ENTER. Then⌷VAR⌷NXT⌷'⌷ B ⌷ENTER⌷+/-. This
isn't how things went when you built the other quadratic solution
(pages 128-129). The difference: When flag –3, the Numerical
Results flag, is *set*, the 48 *evaluates* names during Stack operations. Your name 'b' contains –8, so +/- on 'b' gives 8.

30. 3⌷+/-⌷SPC⌷⍺⌷C⌷⍺⌷F⌷ENTER⌷←⌷π⌷EVAL (result: 'π');
⍺⌷←⌷I⌷EVAL (result: 'i'); and ⍺⌷←⌷E⌷EVAL (result: 'e').
Then 2⌷+/-⌷SPC⌷⍺⌷S⌷⍺⌷F⌷ENTER and repeat these keystrokes....
Numerical values, right? Flag –2 is the Symbolic Constants flag.
Only when Flag -2 is *set* will these constants' names evaluate to
their respective numerical values (unless flag –3 is set, which
overrides a clear flag –2).

31. To PURGe more than one name at a time from your VAR menu, just form a *list* of the names you want to PURGe: [VAR]←[{}] ▮▮X▮▮ ▮SYS1▮ ▮D▮ ▮C▮ ▮EX1▮ ▮A▮ [NXT] ▮B▮ ▮C▮ ▮B▮ ▮VECTO▮ [ENTER]←[PURG] PURGes all VARiables except EQ.

32. Build the expression: [2][ENTER]['][α]←[X][ENTER][X]['][α]←[Y][ENTER] [+]['][α][α][E][X][P][R][α][STO]. Then

    a. [2][+/-]['][α]←[Y][ENTER][X]['][α]←[X][STO] ▮EXPR▮ [EVAL]
          <u>Result</u>: `'2*-(2*y)+y'`

    b. [2][+/-]['] ▮▮X▮▮ [ENTER][X]['][α]←[Y][STO]['] ▮▮X▮▮ ←[PURG]
       ▮EXPR▮ [EVAL]   <u>Result</u>: `'2*x-2*x'`

    c. ['][α]←[T][ENTER][ENTER]['][α]←[X][STO][1][-]['] ▮▮Y▮▮ [STO]
       ▮EXPR▮ [EVAL]   <u>Result</u>: `'2*t+(t-1)'`

    d. ['][α]←[Z][ENTER][ENTER][3]['] ▮▮Y▮▮ [ENTER][X][-]
       ←▮▮X▮▮ [3]←[SWAP][X]['] ▮▮Y▮▮ [ENTER][SWAP][-]←▮▮Y▮▮
       ▮EXPR▮ [EVAL]   <u>Result</u>: `'2*(z-3*y)+(y-3*z)'`

This is just substitution. But notice how the 48 doesn't automatically simplify an algebraic. Notice also the self-referencing name (y) in case **d**: press [EVAL] repeatedly to see its effect....

33. L→V: « OBJ→ →ARRY »

V→L: « OBJ→ OBJ→ DROP →LIST »

Clean up: ⬅[{}] **X** **Y** ENTER ⬅PURG ⬅CLEAR. Then:

⬅« » PRG **TYPE** **OBJ→** **→ARR** ENTER ' α α L ➡→ V α STO; and

⬅« » **OBJ→** **OBJ→** ⬅DROP **→LIST** ENTER ' α α V ➡→ L α STO

Notice that these simple programs are really nothing more than a recording of the keystrokes you use manually. Now test them:

VAR ⬅{}0 ENTER **L→V** ... **V→L** ....looks good;

⬅{}1 SPC 2 SPC 3 ENTER **L→V** ... **V→L** ....OK—but notice that the vector display mode will affect your results;

⬅{}1 SPC 0 SPC ⬅() 1 SPC 0 ENTER **L→V** ... **V→L** ....

OK—but since a vector can't contain real and complex numbers at the same time (unlike a list), it makes everything complex;

⬅{} ENTER **L→V** ...nope—an error. You haven't allowed for the possibility of an empty list (consider how might you do that).

34. LABS: « L→V ABS 1 →ARRY V→L »

   or   « L→V ABS { } + »

So, press (for example) ⬅« » **L→V** α α A B S α SPC ⬅{} ▶ + ENTER ' α α L A B S α STO. Then:

a. ⬅{}1 SPC 2 SPC 3 SPC 4 ENTER **LABS** ....

Result: { 5.47722557505 }

b. ⬅{} ⬅() 1 SPC 1 ▶ ⬅() 3 +/– SPC 4 ENTER **LABS**

Result: { 5.19615242271 }

c. ⬅{} ⬅{}1 SPC 2 ▶ ⬅{}3 SPC 4 ENTER **LABS** ....

Result: Error: Bad Argument type

A vector cannot have vector components.

35. Invoking a directory's name will *not* move you to that directory unless it's in the current PATH ("between you and HOME").

To give a directory named BILL a second name—say, DAVE—just [STO][CST][ON][RCL][→] 'BILL' into 'DAVE'. That way, when you evaluate either BILL or DAVE, you'll be sent to BILL.

36. Here's one way to do it—call this program PHONES:

« DUP NUM CHR OBJ→ »

To key this in: [←][« »][←][ENTER][PRG] **TYPE** [NXT] **NUM** | **CHR** [NXT] [NXT] **OBJ→** [ENTER] ['][α][α][P][H][O][N][E][S][α][STO]

First, DUP makes another copy of the string—so that it's still on the Stack at the end of the program. Then NUM gets the character number of the first character of the string; CHR changes this number back to a one-character string. Then OBJ→ decomposes the string and evaluates its single component character, thus opening the appropriate directory.

To test PHONES, just create a couple of test directories (named with single letters of the alphabet—say, Q, R and S). Then feed PHONES some hypothetical "words" (say, "Quine", "Roberts" and "Simons") to see if it will open up the correct directories. Will it find the directories if you fail to capitalize the target word?

The Wide World of the HP 48

At this point, you know some of the basics of the HP 48. You know about its objects, its Stack, its keyboard, and many of its menus and conveniences. And (if you've been following along and keying in every solution) you've had quite a bit of hands-on practice with the machine. Hopefully you're now more comfortable with it; it shouldn't seem so cryptic or intimidating.

But now your interest in your HP 48 is likely to become a little more narrow. At this point you're probably thinking about some very specific problem or need—the chief reason you bought the machine in the first place. That makes sense; it's why anyone buys a tool.

The problem is, of course, that the 48 is so powerful and sophisticated that it's impossible to cover its potential uses in one book (or even ten books). It is simply impossible to predict all the myriad uses to which you might want to put this machine.

So this book doesn't try to do that. Instead it shows you one major strategy for getting the solution(s) you want—*by building them yourself*, using the building blocks of postscript programming. That's what the rest of this book will concentrate upon.

In doing so, it will also show you many workable methods for organizing memory and using the customizing features of the HP 48 to best advantage.

However, you should keep in mind that keystroke programming is not the only approach you can take to meet your needs on the 48. Indeed, programming may not even be the best way to go.

HP has built in some very powerful (and fairly easy-to-use) applications for topics such as plotting, solving, and symbolic and numerical math; there's no sense re-inventing the wheel after HP has built it for you. However, those applications are extensive enough and useful enough to warrant books of their own, and so they are not covered here.

For more help on the HP 48's built-in applications, here is a suggested reading list:

- To learn more about the graphics capabilities of the machine, including the Plotter, the Solver, and the EquationWriter, you should read *Graphics on the HP 48G/GX*

- If you want to use the HP 48 to help you in your algebra and pre-calculus math studies, you should read *Algebra and Pre-Calculus on the HP 48G/GX*

- If you want to use the 48 to help you in your calculus studies, you should read *Calculus on the HP 48G/GX*

See the back of this book for more information on how to obtain these books.

Now, on to postscript programming....

4 **PROGRAMMING FUNDAMENTALS**

Your "Automation" Options

Now that you've seen some of the tools HP has built into the 48, it's time to learn how to build some for yourself.

A tool in your 48 is an *automated process*—a set of operations, recorded somehow, so that you don't need to re-do them every time you want a similar result. Keep in mind that there are *several* ways to do such "automation"—some of which you've used extensively already:

- By **naming an object**, you effectively record the keystrokes you used to build or calculate its value in the first place. You can reproduce or re-use that value whenever you invoke the name.

- An **algebraic** expression or equation tells the machine to execute a given set of *algebraic operations*—on a given set of *VARiables*—whenever you EVALuate that algebraic object.

- A **postfix program** tells the machine to execute a given set of *commands*—on a given set of *VARiables*, *Stack arguments*, and/or *system parameters*—whenever you EVALuate that program.

- A **list**'s elements can be any objects *and any commands*. And whenever you EVALuate a list, each of its elements is evaluated sequentially, so this is another way to record and execute *commands* on *VARiables*, *Stack arguments* and *system parameters*.

Compare the various methods of "automation" with this table:

Object	Allowed Actions	Source of Values	Range of Results	How You "Run" It
Named Object	EVALuate	any available VARiables	a single value: the value of the object stored in the name	invoke its name
Algebraic Object	any functions	any available VARiables	a single value: the result object	EVALuate it
Postfix Program	any commands	any Stack arguments, available VARiables, system parameters	any value(s), objects and system conditions	EVALuate it or invoke its name
List	any commands	any Stack arguments, available VARiables, system parameters	any value(s), objects and system conditions	EVALuate it

Consider, therefore, how you might best use each type of "automation:"

- To record an object's value, of course, just **name** it as a VARiable.

- To do math with VARiables and functions—generally, any "crunching" intended to give you *a single result*—use **algebraic objects**. They're generally easier than postfix programs to build, read, use, troubleshoot and understand.

  However, though an algebraic is handy, it's not especially "smart." It can do only *functions* (calculations describable in the 48's algebraic syntax). And of course, not all functions are defined for all object types: You can add two strings named a and b with 'a+b', but you can't subtract them with 'a-b'. You'll get an error (and an algebraic generally cannot test for or avoid an error). Also, remember that, unlike most object types, you can't EVALuate an algebraic simply by invoking its name. That just puts it onto the Stack; you must then EVALuate it explicitly.

- Whenever you need to get *multiple results*, manipulate objects or the Stack, adjust system settings (flags, directory structures, etc.)—i.e. *do any non-mathematical but nevertheless "recordable" kinds of operations*—these are jobs for **programs** or **lists**.

  Of the two, a program is the more tailor-made for ready execution, because it does EVALuate when you invoke its name (not so with a list). On the other hand, once you've built a program, you can't *modify* it (edit it) under any sort of automation—only "by hand." But you can readily edit a list via "recorded" commands.

The point here is to choose the most straightforward method for the job. When names and algebraics will suffice, use them. As you learn about programming, remember to save it for when you really need it.

Local Names

To recall the basic idea of building and naming a program, look back at pages 132-135. Of course, not all programs are so simple as those. Sometimes you'll need more. For starters, consider this.

Problem: Define a new function, $q=2x+xy$, so that the 48 can use it within algebraic objects—just like a built-in function.

Solution: ⌜α α ⌐ α Q ( ) X ⌐ ⌜ Y α ▶ ⌐ = 2 X α α X + X X Y [ENTER]. Then press ⌐ [DEF]. That's all there is to it.

Question: What just happened?

Answer: Your HP 48 actually wrote a short little postfix program for you. To see it, just press [VAR] and ⟶ ▉▉ :*

> «
> → x y
> '2*x+x*y'
> »

The DEFINE command built this from your definition. Notice the → x y. That's to tell this UDF (User-Defined Function) how to take your function's arguments off the Stack whenever you evaluate it. The x and y are *local names*—having nothing to do with VARiable names—that the 48 associates *temporarily* with Stack objects.

---

*For the sake of space, this Course will not necessarily show programs formatted identically to your 48's displayed version, but they are entirely equivalent. Line breaks—here and in the machine's display—carry no significance; they are merely formatting for visual clarity.

Keep in mind that you can use a UDF just like any built-in function: Either you put its arguments onto the Stack and invoke just the name: 4 ENTER 5 ⬛ Q ⬛ ; or, you invoke the name and arguments in an algebraic object and evaluate it: ' q(4, 5) ' EVAL

When you invoke the function's name, ⬛ Q ⬛ , the 48 EVALuates the program, q. The first set of instructions it encounters is → x y Essentially, this says to the 48: "Take the objects from the bottom two levels of the Stack (upper one first—it was on the Stack first), and *temporarily* identify them with the names* given after the →."

With the algebraic form, q(4, 5), the *parentheses* tell the 48: "Take the arguments from within the () and put them onto the Stack—in order." At that point, then, the situation is the same as when *you* placed the arguments onto the Stack: q executes, and the → x y instructions proceed as usual.

So that's what a User-Defined Function really is—a postfix program that does just two things:

(i)   assigns one or more Stack arguments to local names;

(ii) uses those local names in calculating a single result.

---

*There's absolutely no requirement to use *lower-case* letters for local names—but it's probably a good habit to develop. It's a convenient reminder that they are indeed *local* names (as opposed to *global* VARiable names, for which you'll likely use *uppercase* characters more often, since the VAR menu displays only in uppercase).

Question: Do you *have* to use DEFINE to build a UDF?

Answer: Not at all. For example, you could have built the ⊲ function yourself: ◄ « → → α ◄ X SPC α ◄ Y SPC ' 2 X α ◄ X + α ◄ X X α ◄ Y ENTER ' α ◄ Q STO.

Now test it: 4 ENTER 5 ▮ ⊲ ▮

or ' α ◄ Q ◄ ( ) 4 ◄ ' 5 ENTER EVAL *No difference.*

Question: Does the "crunching" portion of a UDF have to be a single algebraic object?

Answer: No. In fact, you don't need to use an algebraic at all. This postfix form would work just as well:

```
«
   → x y
   «
      2 x * x y * +
   »
»
```

Key that in:
◄ « → → α ◄ X SPC α ◄ Y ◄ « 2 SPC α ◄ X X α ◄ X SPC α ◄ Y X + ENTER ' ◄ Q STO.

Then try it: 4 ENTER 5 ▮ ⊲ ▮

or ' ▮ ⊲ ▮ ◄ ( ) 4 ◄ ' 5 ENTER EVAL

Notice the "program within a program"—the extra set of « » inside this last version. To declare and assign local names, you use the →, followed by the ordered listing of those names. Then, somehow you must signal the *end* of that listing. The two allowed signals are an algebraic object or the beginning of a program.

Thus, these programs are valid:*

```
«
    → x y
    'SIN(45)+x/y'
    "Bye"
»
```

```
«
    45
    → x y c
    «
        c SIN x y / +
    »
    "Bye"
»
```

```
«
    "Hi"
    → m
    «
        "Good-"
    »
    "bye"
»
```

But these are "illegal:"

```
«
    → x y
    "Hi"
    'SIN(45)+x/y'
»
```

```
«
    → a b
    "Hi"
    «
        a √ b -
    »
»
```

An algebraic object or program segment is the only allowed signal for ending a local names declaration, *because it also defines the environment in which those local names exist.* The names are *local* (and thus not in conflict with your global VARiables) because of the strict boundary you draw around their "jurisdiction." That boundary is the *defining procedure* (the algebraic object or postfix program) *immediately after the names declaration.*

---

*They're valid programs, but notice that they're *not* usable as UDF's: Each of them leaves more than one result on the Stack—a definite no-no for a function.

Each local name is born, lives and dies *within its defining procedure....*

Hmm: Write a program to find $(x+1)(x-1)$; take x from the Stack.

Idea(s):   **(i)**   «
```
DUP 1 + SWAP 1 - *
```
»
Direct, but its argument use is not obvious.

(ii)   «
```
'X' STO X 1 + X 1 - *
```
»
Argument use is more obvious if it's named.

(iii)   «
```
→ x
  «
    x 1 + x 1 - *
  »
»
```
Looks a lot like (ii), but uses a local variable instead of a global VARiable.

(iv)   «
```
→ x
'(x+1)*(x-1)'
»
```
Clearest solution of all, visually.

Cases **(ii)** and **(iii)** do look similar. Indeed, `'X'` STO and → X *are* similar in effect: both store the argument into a name, X. But that name is something entirely different in each case. In case **(ii)** `'X'` is a *global* name and will remain in the current VARiable directory after being used. At the very least, this clutters up that directory, but what if you've already used the name `'X'` to store some other important value? Case **(ii)** would overwrite (destroy) that value. By contrast, in cases **(iii)** and **(iv)**, the *local* name, x, never exists in any VARiable directory; storing the argument in it during its defining procedure does not affect any global name, `'X'`. And the local x *disappears* at the completion of its defining procedure.

So you can see that local names are just as handy as global VARiables for "calling up" input values whenever you need them—so that you needn't try to keep track of them in the Stack meanwhile.

"Ah: So invoking local names works just like invoking global VARiable names?"

No: Recall that when you invoke a VARiable's name, this triggers an automatic EVALuation of the object contained in the name (except if it's an algebraic or a list). But when you invoke a *local* name, there's never an automatic EVALuation; the object contained in the local name is simply put onto the Stack. And you can demonstrate this difference. Try this program that, given two arguments (the old name and the new), renames an existing VARiable in your current directory:

```
«
   → old new
   «
      old RCL new STO old PURGE
   »
»
```

The fact that this program works at all (try it*) says a lot: When it first invokes the local name, old, this simply puts the object *contained* in old onto the Stack. That object is a *global* (VARiable) name—the name you're changing. And clearly this isn't evaluated; if it were, the *value* in that name (whatever it might be) would probably produce an error when the 48 tried to execute RCL with that value as its argument.

---

*You won't see many explicit keystrokes from now on. If you're still not sure how to key in and use a program like this, you may want to review Chapter 3, pages 132-135.

One more thing about local names: Since you can "nest" one program segment inside another, you can therefore "nest" the defining procedures of local names. Look at these examples:

```
«
    → b c
   '√(c^2-b^2)'
»
```

The simple case: Local names c and b exist only inside the defining procedure. This could be a UDF—named LEG or something similar.

```
{
    → b c
   '√(c^2-b^2)'
}
```

Don't forget that lists can do it, too. If you EVALuate this list, a local environment with c and b will be established for the algebraic immediately following—just as with the program version above.

```
«
    → s
    «
      s SQR s 4 *
    »
    → a p
   '22*(a/9+p/30)'
»
```

This is a *sequence* of local name environments: Assigning a single argument (the side of a square) to the local name, s, the first defining procedure uses s to leave *two* results on the Stack (the square's area and perimeter). Since you can't use an algebraic to get more than one result, the first defining procedure must be a program. When it finishes (and s and its environment are gone), the two results are assigned to local names a and p for the final calculation in an algebraic procedure.

```
«
   → x y z
   «
      x SQR y SQR + √
      → r
      'π*r^2*z'
      '√(x^2+y^2+z^2)'
   »
   SWAP
»
```

This is a *nesting* of local environments: The first procedure assigns arguments to x, y and z, then does a calculation on x and y and assigns that to another, *inner* procedure environment (the first algebraic), to calculate a cylindrical volume. The end of that first algebraic is the end of the inner environment; at that point, r disappears. But the outer environment still exists, so the program can still use x, y and z until it encounters a » to end *that* environment. *Notice* that the local names from the outer procedure (x, y and z) exist within the inner procedure, too—*because they existed when the inner environment was created.*

```
«
   → b c
   '√(c^2)-√(b^2+LEG(b, c)^2)'
»
```

Here, within an environment with local names b and c, you invoke a UDF, LEG (from the previous page). So LEG EVALuates, creating an environment for *its* local names, b and c. *Do those conflict* with the b and c created above? No. Unlike nesting (where all commands creating the inner environment are executed *within* the outer environment), when you invoke the name of another, already-created program, any local environment that program creates will be *outside* the invoking environment. Therefore, LEG cannot "see" the local names created above. It will interpret the b and c in LEG(b, c) as the *global* VARiables names 'b' and 'c' and assign *those* to its local names.

Program Design

Obviously, you can do a lot more with a 48 program than just straight-ahead arithmetic with a few arguments. It's time to explore the 48's inventory of programming tools—loops, conditional tests, etc. But first, some general comments....

No matter what kind of machine you're programming, you generally work through certain basic considerations when *designing* the program—before you even begin to write the code itself.

A *general* program design checklist might look something like this:

Define the outputs   Identify the results the machine is to calculate—the acceptable **ranges** of values and their **order** and **format** of presentation.

Define the inputs   Identify the information the user will supply to the machine—acceptable **ranges** of values and the **order** and **format** of input.

Set your strategy   Identify the critical approach and processes.

Subdivide tasks:

Prepare	Prepare memory, system parameters;
Get inputs	Prompt for, check and store inputs;
Process inputs	Calculate, trap undesired errors;
Give outputs	Format, recall results;
Clean up	Reset memory, system parameters, etc.

This checklist can help when you're programming the 48, especially the step where you **set your strategy.** If you clearly define that strategy first, you'll have no problem matching it properly with specific tools in the 48.

Also:

- There's no way around it: In postfix programs, you'll have to use some postfix notation. And it's not intuitively easy to read:

  1 2 +   instead of   1+2

  So *in every solution you see here*, force yourself to "walk" mentally through the program steps: Envision the Stack (do it on paper if it helps) and track the arguments as they come and go. If you want to be a programmer, you must learn the language.

- What's the difference between a built-in command and a program that you build and name?   ...Think about it....

  Not much, right? So if you don't find, say, a certain handy Stack command already built-into the 48—no problem—build it and name it yourself! In this way, you can literally *add to the tool box of commands* in your 48. And then, of course, you can use those tools to create still others, and so on.

  The 48 is well suited for such *modular* programming: no single program structure need be very long or intricate. Instead, it can invoke other small programs *as commands*, which, if you've designed them consistently, will behave as such (take arguments, return results, generate predictable errors). Your design strategy simplifies immensely if you consistently mimic built-in tools.

First, look at some "warmer-uppers" to see how that design checklist applies to your modular 48 workshop....

Problem: Write two programs, LMAX and LSUM, that do for lists what the commands RNRM and CNRM do for vectors.

Solution: <u>Outputs</u>. Each program should return a real number.

<u>Inputs</u>. Each program will take one argument (Stack Level 1)—a list of real or complex numbers (one type only). Any type error should be reported

<u>Strategy</u>. Convert list to array, then RNRM or CNRM.

<u>Subdivide tasks</u>. No need to <u>prepare</u> anything. These programs should use the current memory configuration and flag settings, just like built-in commands. No <u>prompt</u> for the input—postfix commands assume the argument is on the Stack already. And no <u>input checks</u>; CNRM or RNRM will catch object-type errors. Each program consumes its argument and leaves its <u>result</u> on the Stack—just like a built-in command. No need to <u>clean up</u>—you didn't mess up anything.

<u>The code</u>.

LMAX:
```
«
    OBJ→ →ARRY RNRM
»
```

LSUM:
```
«
    OBJ→ →ARRY CNRM
»
```

All the formal design may seem like a lot of fuss over those rather simple programs, but—like anything else—if you do it consistently, it will become automatic. More to the point, notice how many of the steps in the design checklist are taken care of by using or mimicking the built-in commands. Now LMAX and LSUM will behave as commands, too—especially if you've stored them in the HOME directory (so that they're accessible from any other directory).   Try some more....

Problem: Write a program to compute a unit vector in the same direction as a given vector.

Solution: UNIT: «
              DUP ABS ∕
          »

This consumes the argument and leaves a result—for any non-zero real number, unit, complex number, vector or array (and depending on flag –3, an empty name or algebraic could be acceptable, too). For other argument types—or zero values—you'll get an error. *All of this is consistent with the behavior of the built-in ABS function.*

Problem: Write a program to double an array and subtract 1 from every element.

Solution: DS1: «
              2 * DUP 1 CON -
          »

Again, this consumes the argument and leaves a result. And it works on several argument types.

When you need multiple arguments—or need to do more "horsing around" on the Stack—that's when to consider using local names to keep things clear and tidy....

Problem: Write a program that splits a given character string into two substrings before the given character position.

Solution: SPLIT: «
                         → S P
                         «
                             S 1 P 1 - SUB
                             S P S SIZE SUB
                         »
                     »

Follow the progress of events on the Stack (work on your postfix reading skills). Notice how the program prepares two arguments for the built-in command, SUB.

As usual, the program consumes its own arguments. Indeed, local names accomplish this very nicely: they remove the arguments from the Stack right away, keeping them available by name, then disappearing with them when their procedure ends.*

Notice also that the two results (the two parts of the original string) are left on the Stack so that *the reverse process* (combining them) *is as easy as possible* ([+]). This, too, is a typical trait of the built-in commands (recall how OBJ→ works so well in this respect).

---

*But is SPLIT a User-Defined Function? No—it leaves more than one result.

You've been designing new commands that relied upon built-in commands they invoke to set their input limits and generate errors. But what if you want to create a command with *more flexible* tolerances ("smarter") than any built-in command it invokes?

Conditional Tests

The most basic kind of program flexibility is a machine's ability to *make decisions*. That is, it can change its course of action "on the fly"—basing its decisions upon information it encounters *during execution*. The 48 makes a decision by asking a question that can be answered by "yes" or "no." The command that asks the question is a *conditional test*, and it returns a 1 result for "yes" or a 0 result for "no."

Do This: Press PRG TEST and look through the resulting menu....

Each item asks a question* answerable by "yes" or "no" (1 or 0). And most of these questions *compare* one value with another, therefore demanding two arguments.**

For example, the > command asks: "Is the object in Stack Level 2 *greater than* that in Level 1?"

---

*Actually the SF, CF, TYPE and NOT commands are *not* tests (yes-or-no questions) at all, but you use them so often in conjunction with the other tests that they appear on this menu for convenience.

**There are a few *single*-argument tests, however—the flag tests (FS?, FC?, FS?C and FC?C)—where the only argument needed is the number of the flag to be tested.

Of course, when you're conducting such comparative conditional tests, the two argument objects must be *comparable*. You can't compare apples with oranges; nor an array with a character string. In general, the two objects being compared should be of the same type.

Examples: **<u>Stack arguments</u>**   **<u>Test</u>**

    2:        11   <
    1:        19

<u>Result:</u> 1   "*Yes*—the object in Level 2 is *less than* the object in Level 1."

    2:        11   → a b
    1:        19   «
                            a b <
                      »

<u>Result:</u> 1   The same test as above, but using local names and a program procedure.

    2:        11   → a b
    1:        19   'a<b'
<u>Result:</u> 1   Same again, with an algebraic procedure.

    2:        11   >
    1:        19
<u>Result:</u> 0   "*No*—Level 2 is *not* greater than Level 1."

    2: "AARDVARK"   <
    1:    "zymurgy"
<u>Result:</u> 1   For strings, "less than" means *alphabetically first* (note: "Z" comes *before* "a").

Stack arguments	**Test**

2:       (11,0)   ==
1:         11

Result: 1   == tests for *equality of value* (the single =
symbol is to build algebraic equations).

2:       (11,0)   SAME
1:         11

Result: 0   SAME tests for *exactly identical* objects.

2:       'B^2'   ≥
1:     '4*A*C'

Result: 'B^2≥4*A*C' A test comparing expressions
acts as an *operator*, combining the two arguments into a
new expression (recall that you built a quadratic expression similarly: 'B^2-4*A*C'). To get the yes-or-no (1 or
0) answer to the inequality test, you must EVALuate it
with numerical values in each VARiable (A, B and C).

2:        44   AND
1:         0

Result: 0   The logical operators can test combinations of real values. Each value is taken
simply as non-zero (true) or zero (false).

2:        0   → a b
1:       64   '(a OR b) AND b'

Result: 1   You can build tests of your own like this.

Branching

So now you know how to tell your 48 to test values—ask questions....

Question: *What can it do* with the answers? How do you give it one set of commands ("Plan A") for a "yes" and another set ("Plan B")—or maybe none at all—for "no"?

Answer(s):   You use one of the four IF program structures, all available in the (PRG) **BRCH** (BRanCH) menu:*

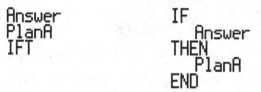

```
Answer              IF
PlanA                 Answer
IFT                 THEN
                        PlanA
                    END
```

In each of the IF-THEN structures, the 48 evaluates PlanA only if the Answer to the test is *true* (1). If Answer is false (0), the structures do nothing.

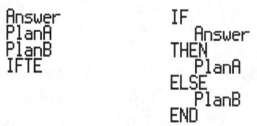

```
Answer              IF
PlanA                 Answer
PlanB               THEN
IFTE                    PlanA
                    ELSE
                        PlanB
                    END
```

In each of the IF-THEN-ELSE structures, the 48 will evaluate PlanA if the Answer is true (1). But if the Answer is false (0), the 48 evaluates PlanB instead.

---

*The various menus in the (PRG) toolbox offer a wealth of typing aids for programmable commands, many of which you can use in this chapter. Be sure to use them—and explore them, including their shifted menu items—as you build programs here.

Example: Write a program that leaves the square of the Level-1 argument only if its absolute value is ≥ 1 and ≤ 5.

Solution:

```
«
   → x
   «
      'ABS(x)≥1 AND ABS(x)≤5'
      'x^2'
      IFT
   »
»
```

IFT is the postfix IF-THEN. It finds its arguments on the Stack:

```
2:   'ABS(x)≥1 AND ABS(x)≤5'
1:                    'x^2'
```

The first argument is the test, which evaluates either to 1 or 0. The second argument is "Plan A," the object to be evaluated only if the test evaluates to *true* (1). In either case, like other commands, IFT *consumes* its arguments. Note that your "Plan A" (the second argument) could be a program (or any other object) instead of an algebraic: If it were a program, IFT would find the Stack like this:

```
2:   'ABS(x)≥1 AND ABS(x)≤5'
1:                « x SQ »
```

Programs and algebraics are both valid object types for *procedural* arguments such as these. And you could, of course, use a program for the conditional test, too:

```
«
   → x
   «
      « x ABS 1 ≥ x ABS 5 ≤ AND »
      « x SQ »
      IFT
   »
»
```

Question: How would the solution to the previous problem look if you were to use the more readable IF...THEN...END structure rather than the strictly postfix IFT?

Answer: Probably something like this:

```
«
   → x
   «
      IF
         'ABS(x)≥1 AND ABS(x)≤5'
      THEN
         x SQ
      END
   »
»
```

IF...THEN...END doesn't expect Stack arguments; it's probably easier to read. Part of its readability makes it convenient to key in, too: Since it doesn't look for Stack arguments, it doesn't force you to put your "Plan A" into the form of a procedure object (program or algebraic). Instead, the 48 simply takes all instructions between the **THEN** and the **END** to be part of your "Plan A." Thus, at the very least, it can save you the keying in of the extra pair of ' ' or « ».

So IFT and IF...THEN...END are your two options for using the result of a test to decide whether or not to execute a certain set of instructions.

Often, though, you want to use a single test to choose between *two* different courses of action ("Plan A" and "Plan B")....

Problem: Write a program that negates (changes the sign of) the Level-1 argument if it's a real-valued array* but drops it from the Stack if it's anything else.

Solution:

```
«
   DUP TYPE
   → x t
   «
      't==3'
      '-x'
      0
      IFTE
   »
»
```

IFTE is just like IFT—except that you need an extra argument on the Stack for the "else" case:

```
3:              't==3'
2:              '-x'
1:              0
```

The first argument onto the Stack is the conditional test ('t==3' asks "is t equal to 3?"). Next comes the "Plan A" object (for *true* answer), then the "Plan B" object (for *false*). IFTE consumes all of its arguments. Note also that IFTE can be used as an algebraic *function:*

```
«
   DUP TYPE
   → x t
   'IFTE(t==3, -x, 0)'
»
```

Just as with any other function, the arguments in IFTE's argument list correspond to those you would normally prepare for it on the Stack. IFTE is unique among the four IF-THEN structures in having this algebraic form.

---

*To test the type of the given object, use the TYPE command: It will return a 3 for a real-valued array (look up and read about TYPE in your HP manuals to see all the various values it can return).

IF...THEN...END is a more readable version of the postfix IFT, so IF...THEN...ELSE...END is a more readable form of the postfix IFTE. Here's how you might solve the previous problem by using the IF...THEN...ELSE...END structure:

```
«
    DUP TYPE
    → x t
    «
        IF
            't==3'
        THEN
            '-x'
        ELSE
            0
        END
    »
»
```

Or (without local names):

```
«
    IF
        DUP TYPE 3 ==
    THEN
        NEG
    ELSE
        DROP 0
    END
»
```

So those are your four choices for branching *one* or *two* ways, depending upon the outcome of one conditional test. But what if you want to branch one of *several* different ways—using several tests?

Problem: Write a program to return a character string describing the magnitude of a given real value.

Solution:

```
«
    ABS XPON
  → m
    «
        CASE
            'm≤0'
                THEN
                    "Ones"
                END
            'm==1'
                THEN
                    "Tens"
                END
            'm==2'
                THEN
                    "Hundreds"
                END
            'm==3'
                THEN
                    "Thousands"
                END
            'm==4'
                THEN
                    "Tens of thousands"
                END
            'm==5'
                THEN
                    "Hundreds of thousands"
                END
            'm==6'
                THEN
                    "Millions"
                END
            "Several gadzillion" 1000 .1 BEEP
        END
    »
»
```

In a **CASE** statement, each case has its own test; the items following it
(between each **THEN** and **END**) are evaluated only if that test result is
true. The final (optional) items are evaluated if *no* test results are true.

You've seen how to use conditional tests and branching to check object types and ranges and proceed accordingly. But what if you don't know all the possible problems? Sometimes, you need to try your commands and deal with the errors as they arise....

Problem: Write a program to perform a simple division, but substitute a character string if the attempted division causes any error.

Solution:

```
«
    IFERR
        /
    THEN
        DROP2 "Not a number"
    END
»
```

IFERR (IF ERRor) is much like the IF-THEN command, but rather than obtaining a conditional test result from the commands between it and THEN, IFERR checks to see if those commands generate an error. If so, IFERR causes a skip to the THEN part (DROP2 "Not a Number" here). If there's no error, the original commands (/) are completed and those between THEN and END are skipped.

There's also IFERR...THEN...ELSE...END. So now you can trap errors—even if you can't predict in advance what they might be.

That's your basic repertoire of branching devices. Don't worry—you'll get lots more practice in the quiz coming up. But first, consider another important set of programming structures....

Looping

One of the most valuable features of any computing device is its ability to accurately and tirelessly *repeat* a series of commands....

Look: You can use one of these six loop structures on the 48:

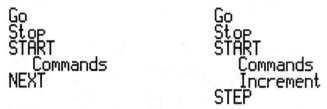

To repeat a set of Commands *a known number of times*, you can *count* from one value, Go, to another value, Stop—by ones (START...NEXT) or by any Increment (START...STEP).

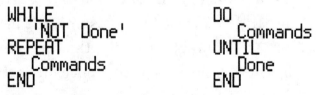

You can also *name the loop counter* (here it's Index), so that you can use its changing value in your repeated Commands.

```
WHILE              DO
    'NOT Done'         Commands
REPEAT             UNTIL
    Commands           Done
END                END
```

Or, for an *unknown number of repetitions*, just repeat until a given exit *condition* is satisfied: WHILE...REPEAT...END tests for the exit condition at the beginning of the command loop; DO...UNTIL...END tests for it at the end of the loop.

Try some examples of each kind of loop....

Problem: Write a program to sum the elements of a given list.

Solution:
```
«
  OBJ→ 2 SWAP
  START
    +
  NEXT
»
```

This uses a simple START...NEXT loop. Name this program SUML, and try it on this list:

$$\{ \ 27 \ 8 \ 9 \ 43 \ \}$$

The first command, OBJ→, puts the list's elements and their *element count* (4) onto the Stack:

```
5:    27              6:    27
4:     8              5:     8
3:     9              4:     9
2:    43              3:    43
1:     4              2:     2
                      1:     4
```

Next, the program puts a 2 onto the Stack and SWAPs positions with the 4. Your loop counters are now ready. The START will read (and consume) them, thus counting from 2 to 4* and performing the commands inside the loop (in this case it's just +), once for each count.

---

*Notice that the number of additions necessary to sum all the elements is one less than the number of elements. This is why your loop count goes from 2 to 4, not 1 to 4. You could, of course, count from 1 to 3 (or –45 to –43, or any other 3-count interval), but it's simplest to use the element count (4) produced by OBJ→ as the "end" of the count.

Question: How could you change the SUML program so that it would correctly ignore any error arising from trying to add with an "unaddable" type of object?

Answer: Put an IFERR...THEN...END structure inside the loop:

In this version, you put an extra value (0) onto the Stack—so that the program will start with a valid "running total" even if the very first list element it encounters is "unaddable." Here's the Stack as START finds it:*

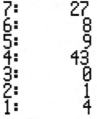

The commands inside the loop are now the IFERR structure, which will allow the + if that doesn't cause an error, but will substitute a SWAP DROP to dispose of any element causing an "unaddability" error.**

---

*Since you've inserted your own starting value (0), the number of additions necessary to sum all elements is now *equal* to the number of elements. So your count goes from 1 to 4 this time.

**Still, your "sum of all elements" may not turn out to be a real number: Recall what + does with character strings, complex numbers, etc.: Those object types will *not* cause errors here.

Problem: Write a program to count (in the display) from any two given real values, with any real increment.

Solution:

```
«
   → i j d
   «
      i i j
      START
         DUP 1 DISP 1 WAIT d +
         d
      STEP
   »
»
```

This solution uses the START...STEP loop—where you specify the *increment* of your count as well as its starting and ending values. Name the program COUNT and try it with various starting, ending and increment values.*

First the program takes your three arguments (beginning, ending and increment values, respectively) from the Stack and puts them into local names. Then it puts the beginning value (i) back—as the first running total to be displayed—then the beginning *and* ending values (i and j), as consumable arguments for START. Then, inside the loop, you DISPlay the running total on display line 1 and pause via the WAIT command for 1 second. Then you add the increment value, d, to the running total, then give d also as the consumable argument for STEP (so that it knows how to increment its own count), and that ends the loop.

---

*How does it handle negative values? Non-integer values? Non-real values?

So one solution for the COUNT program is to build and increment your own counter on the Stack. You must do that if you use a START...STEP loop, because the count it conducts is hidden and inaccessible to you. But is there another, easier way to display a count?

Sure: Use a FOR...STEP structure instead. In that kind of loop, its own count *is* accessible to you—via the *name* you give it.

Watch:
```
«
  → i j d
  «
     i j
     FOR c
        c 1 DISP 1 WAIT
        d
     STEP
  »
»
```

After assigning arguments to local names, you enter a FOR loop, supplying begin and end count values (i and j). In a FOR loop, you declare a *local name* (existing only inside that loop), to represent the current value of the loop's count. In this example, you *declare* the count name (c); then you *use* it to put the count onto the Stack for display. Thus you need no explicit addition to increment the Stack count: When you end the loop (d is the argument for STEP, as before), on the next cycle the *loop structure itself* will have incremented its own count, c. Invoking that name, c, puts the current count onto the Stack; the displayed count *is* the loop count.*

---

*Notice that if COUNT were to offer an increment of 1 only, you'd use a FOR...NEXT structure and dispense with d. Realize also that, within the loop, you can do any calculation you want with c; it's an entirely usable local name—with a local environment *nested* inside that of i, j and d.

So that's how to design programs to cycle through a known number of loops. But what if you *don't* know that number?

Problem: Write a program that drops objects off the Stack until it encounters a character string or empties the Stack.

Solution:

```
«
   WHILE
      DEPTH
      « DUP TYPE 2 ≠ »
      0
      IFTE
      DEPTH 1 > AND
   REPEAT
      DROP
   END
»
```

First, notice the IFTE structure within the WHILE test: To avoid an error, only if the Stack is not empty (i.e. if DEPTH gives a non-zero value) will the TYPE command test the Level-1 object. Then, since the Stack will at that point contain at least the truth value (0 or 1) from the TYPE test, the test to see if the Stack was not originally empty must actually test whether its DEPTH is now > 1. *Both* the TYPE test AND the non-empty Stack test must be true in order for the WHILE...REPEAT...END loop to begin; if the WHILE test returns 0 on very first time, the program will end without the commands in the loop having executed even once. This suits the problem: With a character string already at Level 1 (or with an empty Stack), the program *shouldn't* do anything.

Again: A WHILE...REPEAT...END loop tests its condition before entering the loop itself. By contrast, consider this...

Problem: Write a solution that produces two *odd* random integers between 0 and 100.

Solution:*
```
IRAND:    «                    ODD?:  «
            RAND 100 * IP              2 MOD
          »                          »
```

```
«
    0 0
    DO
        DROP2 IRAND IRAND
    UNTIL
        DUP2 ODD? SWAP ODD? AND
    END
»
```

Unlike WHILE...REPEAT...END, a DO...UNTIL...END loop is appropriate here, since it always executes its loop commands *at least once* (even if your first two values come up odd, you do need to generate them, no?). So the conditional test comes *after* the loop's commands.

Practice your postfix reading as you follow the commands. Notice how you put two start values (0 and 0) onto the Stack before entering the loop. This is to allow for the first commands inside the loop, which keep the Stack clean by dropping two previous, unacceptable values.

---

*Notice how you assist the program with two smaller programs: IRAND generates a random integer between 0 and 100; and ODD? tests an integer value for "odd-ness," returning a truth value (i.e. either 0 or not 0)—just like a built-in test. Of course, you could instead include their contents twice in the main program, but that's not as good a use of the 48's modular extensibility .

Quiz

That's a brief tour of the programming structures available to you. Now put it all together with these practice problems.

1. Write two programs, one with local names and one without, to calculate $\dfrac{(A+B)(A-B)}{C}$, given arguments A, B, C (in that order).

2. Unlike the two-argument comparative tests, the four built-in flag tests (FS?, FC?, FS?C and FC?C) are not valid in functional (algebraic) form. That is, you can't build expressions such as `'FS?(-2) AND FC?(-3)'`—though these might indeed be handy in your programs. So, *write your own:* write four UDF's to allow you effectively to use flag tests in algebraics. In general, how might you make various system flags more convenient?

3. Write a new conditional test, called LIST?, that tests whether a given object is a list. Then use LIST? to write another test, called FLST?, that tests whether a given object is a non-empty list.

4. Write programs that take a given string and:

    (i)   reverse the order of the characters;
    (ii)   change all lowercase characters to uppercase;
    (iii) change all uppercase characters to lowercase;
    (iv)   change both cases simultaneously.

5. What's the primary use of a list as a procedure object?

6. Write a program that deletes from a given string...

    (i)   all leading occurrences

    (ii)   all trailing occurrences

...of a given character (another string—the second argument).

7. Write a program that waits for you to press the α key.

8. Write a program that takes a given list and a given conditional test procedure (in that order) and applies the test to each element of the list, returning a "filtered" version of the list—containing only the elements that satisfy the test.

9. Recall the alphabetical directory structure described in problem **36** on page 149. Write a program that returns the object stored in a given name in one of those 26 alphabetical directories.

10. How would you build your own version of OBJ→?

11. Write four programs that take a given real-valued array (not a vector) and *reverse* or *sort* a specified row/column.

Quiz Answers

1. As is usually the case with programming, there are many ways to solve a given problem. First, using local names:

```
«                                    or   «
   → a b c                                   → a b c
   «                                         '(a+b)*(a-b)/c'
      a b + a b - * c /                    »
   »
»
```

```
«                                    or   «
   → a b c                                   → a b c
   «                                         '(a^2-b^2)/c'
      a SQ b SQ - c /                       »
   »
»
```

Then, without local names:

```
«                                    or   «
   ROT ROT DUP2 +                             ROT SQ ROT SQ -
   ROT ROT - * SWAP /                         SWAP /
»                                         »
```

2. Simply "repackage" each built-in command:

```
Fs?:  «                    Fc?:  «
         → f                        → f
         «                          «
            f FS?                      f FC?
         »                          »
      »                          »
```

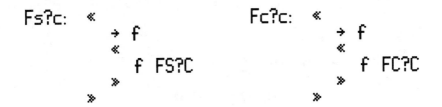

```
Fs?c:    «
           → f
         «
             f FS?C
         »
     »
```

```
Fc?c:    «
           → f
         «
             f FC?C
         »
     »
```

Note that you could also build little routines to test certain sets of system flags. For example, flags –45 through –48 set the number of decimal places in the current display format; flags –49 and –50 represent the format itself. So you could write routines named, say, DGTS? and FMT?, to test these parameters (recall how you extracted the binary word size similarly from its system flags on page 104).

3.   LIST?:   «
                  TYPE 5 ==
              »

     FLST?:   «
                  IF
                      DUP LIST?
                  THEN
                      SIZE 0 >
                  ELSE
                      DROP 0
                  END
              »

4. **(i)**

```
«
  → s
  «
    "" 1 s SIZE
    FOR i
      s i i SUB SWAP +
    NEXT
  »
»
```

(ii)

```
«
  → s
  «
    "" 1 s SIZE
    FOR i
      s i i SUB NUM
      → n
      'IFTE(n≥97 AND n≤122, n-32, n)'
      CHR +
    NEXT
  »
»
```

(iii)

```
«
  → s
  «
    "" 1 s SIZE
    FOR i
      s i i SUB NUM
      → n
      'IFTE(n≥65 AND n≤90, n+32, n)'
      CHR +
    NEXT
  »
»
```

(iv)

```
«
  → s
  «
    "" 1 s SIZE
    FOR i
      s i i SUB NUM
      → n
      'IFTE(n≥97 AND n≤122, n-32, IFTE(n≥65
          AND n≤90, n+32, n))'
CHR +
NEXT
  »
»
```

5. Lists are useful to evaluate as directory PATHs. For example, to DOSTUFF in a directory, DIR1, that's *not* in the current PATH, simply save the current PATH (it's a *list* of directory names, remember) and then later *EVALuate* it, to get back to that PATH:

```
... PATH
→ whereiwas
«
    HOME DIR1 DOSTUFF
    whereiwas EVAL
» ...
```

6. (i)
```
«
→ ch
«
WHILE
    DUP NUM CHR ch ==
REPEAT
    2 OVER SIZE SUB
END
»
»
```

(ii)
```
«
→ ch
«
WHILE
    DUP SIZE DUP2 DUP SUB ch ==
REPEAT
    1 SWAP 1 - SUB
END
DROP
»
»
```

A WHILE loop is appropriate for these, since you don't know if you'll need to trim off *any* characters from the string; the test comes *before* the action. Note that only one of the two arguments (the character to be trimmed) is put into a local name. The original string is "whittled down" (by SUB), one character each loop cycle; the previous cycle's result is the argument for the next cycle.

7. Here's one way:

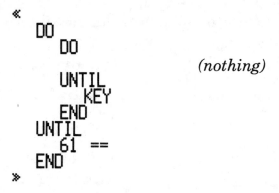

```
«
   DO
      DO
      UNTIL
         KEY
      END
   UNTIL
      61  ==
   END
»
```

(nothing)

The KEY command returns a **0** if no key is pressed or a key location (row-column) code and a 1 if a key is pressed. You're looking for key code 61 (row 6, column 1), using a nested pair of DO... UNTIL loops. The inner loop repeats until any key is pressed; the outer loop repeats until the *correct* keycode (61) is detected. See your HP manual for more about the related WAIT command, too.

8. LFLTR:

```
«
   → list test
   «
      { } 1 list SIZE
      FOR i
         list i GET DUP
         IF
            test EVAL
         THEN
            +
         ELSE
            DROP
         END
      NEXT
   »
»
```

You know the number of cycles through the loop from the SIZE of the given list. Note that you must EVALuate the test procedure explicitly (invoking a local name won't do this for you).

Notice also that the HP 48 offers another way to accomplish this, via the DOLIST command:

LFLTR:
```
«
   → list test
   «
      list 1
      «
         DUP
         IF
            test EVAL NOT
         THEN
            DROP
         END
      »
      DOLIST
   »
»
```

You'll find a lot of interesting list commands in Chapter 17 of your User's Guide (and you'll see more uses of them in Chapter 6 here).

9.
```
«
   → n
   «
      { HOME } n →STR 1 2 SUB
      OBJ→ + n + RCL
   »
»
```

The strategy here is to build a PATH list to the given name and then RCL that path—rather than EVALuate it—thus staying in the current directory (alternatively, you could use the "remember-and return" strategy shown in problem 5). Notice how you extract the single-letter directory name by first converting the given name to a string.

10.

```
Obj→:  «
          DUP TYPE
          CASE
             0 ==
                THEN
                    Real→
                END
             1 ==
                THEN
                    Cplx→
                END
             2 ==
                THEN
                    Str→
                END
             3 ==
                THEN
                    Rarr→
                END
             4 ==
                THEN
                    Carr→
                END
             5 ==
                THEN
                    List→
                END
              ... (etc.)
          END
       »
```

Or: Obj→: «
```
          → ob
          «
            { Real→ Cplx→ Str→ ...(etc.)... }
            ob TYPE GET EVAL
          »
       »
```

Of course, you also need to define each of the specific routines, Real→, Cmplx→, etc. And then to change how a certain object type "decomposes," you'd simply edit that specific routine—not Obj→.

11. RevRw: «
```
        → r
    «
        r ROW- OBJ→ OBJ→ DROP →LIST
        REVLIST OBJ→ →ARRY r ROW+
    »
»
```

RevCl: «
```
        → c
    «
        c COL- OBJ→ OBJ→ DROP →LIST
        REVLIST OBJ→ →ARRY c COL+
    »
»
```

SrtRw: «
```
        → r
    «
        r ROW- OBJ→ OBJ→ DROP →LIST
        SORT OBJ→ →ARRY r ROW+
    »
»
```

SrtCl: «
```
        → c
    «
        c COL- OBJ→ OBJ→ DROP →LIST
        SORT OBJ→ →ARRY c COL+
    »
»
```

Notice the assumed order of inputs—the array, then the row/ column number. But only the latter is taken as a local variable; the array just sits on the Stack, with one of its rows or columns first extracted, then replaced.

5 **CUSTOMIZING YOUR WORKSHOP**

Labor-Saving Devices

A calculator as powerful as the 48 is certainly a labor-saving device. But that very power offers you so many choices that the keystrokes simply to *make* those choices soon become laborious, too—unless you take advantage of certain built-in features.

For example, it's great to be able to build and name a lot of new commands. But then you may have several pages in your VARiable menu to "leaf through" whenever you want to use one of those commands— which defeats the convenience of the menu for quick typing/execution. What to do? Use *custom menus* to group together the commands you typically *use* together, thus reducing your need for [NXT]'s and [←][PREV]'s.

This is just one example of the many labor-saving devices the 48 offers you. You set up certain assumptions about your particular needs and work habits, so that the machine will do more of what you want with fewer keystrokes.

So as you study (and in some cases, review) these features, consider how you might best use them. Weigh the labor you save with a tool or configuration against the labor you expend to build it and use it. That's the key question to ask yourself. This chapter on customizing is really about *optimizing* (not maximizing or minimizing); the best solution for one situation isn't necessarily that same for another.

Input Shortcuts

You've already seen most of the ways to ease and shorten your use of the 48's densely-packed keyboard, but here's a good one-glance recap.

Alpha Modes

α *Normal single-stroke alpha mode.* Normally, pressing α N yields N; pressing α ← N yields n; and pressing α → N yields μ. Thus, each key may have three alpha "meanings." But the alpha mode only lasts for the next keystroke.

α ← α *Lower-case single-stroke alpha mode.* When you need to input many lower-case alpha characters, you can change what the ← key does by pressing α ← α. Thereafter, until you press ENTER or CANCEL, α N yields n and α ← N yields N. The ENTER or CANCEL returns the alpha-shift keys to normal. The alpha mode lasts just one keystroke.

α α *Normal alpha-lock mode.* This locks the keyboard into alpha mode until a third press of α (or ENTER or CANCEL) releases it.

α α ← α *Lower-case alpha-lock mode.* This locks the keyboard into lower-case alpha mode for the duration of the Command Line.

Flag –60 affects the action of the four alpha modes. When it's clear, they operate as described above. But when it's set, the single-stroke alpha modes are disabled; a single α enters alpha-lock mode until a second press of α (or ENTER or CANCEL) releases it.

The Interactive Stack

▲   Allows you to review the contents of the Stack and manipulate it directly Among the many handy Stack tools are these:

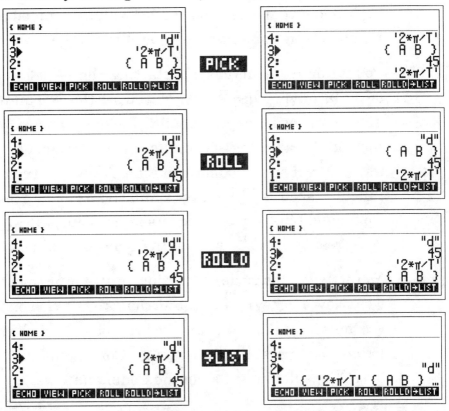

Remember, too, that **ECHO** copies a selected level of the Stack right into your Command Line, to save you from retyping it. With the 48, there are more than one way to do most things.

Command Line Entry Modes

A built-in menu item normally evaluates immediately, making it impossible to use it as a typing aid. In fact, the only keystrokes that won't normally evaluate immediately are numbers and characters. Thus, ④ SPC ⑤ ⊞ results in a 9.

PRG You can activate this mode by starting a list (←{ }) or program (← « ») or via → ENTRY. When you see the **PRG** annunciator, any menu key for any _command, function_, or _VARiable_ will—instead of evaluating—insert its name, surrounded by spaces, at the cursor on the Command Line. A keyboard command or function (such as ⊞) behaves similarly: its name goes into the Command Line, surrounded by spaces. Thus, → ENTRY ④ SPC ⑤ ⊞ results in 4 5 + ◆ on the Command Line.

ALG You activate this mode by starting an algebraic object or name (′). Now any key or menu item that is a _function_ or _VARiable_ (i.e. anything allowed in an algebraic object) will be inserted, _without spaces_, at the cursor on the Command Line. Thus, ′ ④ ⊞ ⑤ results in '4+5' on the Command Line.

ALG PRG You can turn on this mode by pressing → ENTRY → ENTRY while in normal mode, or ′ while in **PRG** mode, or → ENTRY while in **ALG** mode. Here, any _command_ key or menu item behaves as it would in **PRG** mode, while any _function or variable_ key or menu item behaves as it would in **ALG** mode.

You cannot type an _operation_, such as CANCEL, into the Command Line (that's the difference between _commands_ and _operations_). To determine if a keystroke is an operation, command, or function, see the Operation Index in your HP manual.

Special Entry Modes

→MATRIX The Matrix Writer makes entering and editing two-dimensional arrays extremely easy and intuitive. You are less likely to make careless mistakes if you use the MW instead of the Command Line to enter arrays. See your HP manual for details.

←EQUATION The Equation Writer allows you to enter any algebraic object—however complex—in a visual format similar to that on paper. The EW itself has a special entry mode:

←{} Within the EW, you can disable the implicit parentheses by pressing ←{}. This allows you to enter polynomials without having to press ▶ after each exponent. You can then reactivate the normal, implicit parentheses feature by pressing ←{} once again.

For more practice with the EW, see your HP manual or read *Graphics on the HP 48G/GX*, by Ray Depew

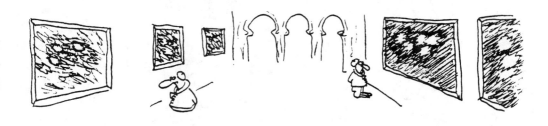

The VAR Menu, CHOOSing and →[MEMORY]

Keep in mind that for many built-in tools, there are input forms that make your specifying of variables and their contents much easier, via the **CHOOS** box.

In fact this is true even for variables and directories in general. Of course, each directory has its own VAR menu, where all of the objects you create in that directory are listed—and whenever you need quick access either to the object's name or the object itself, it's usually easiest to use the VAR menu. But for a more complete tool that surveys your directories, variables and their contents, try the Variable Browser— press →[MEMORY]....

This input form allows you to create, edit, move, copy, purge or measure the size of the objects in your HP 48's memory. (In Chapter 6, there are some programs which allow you to do similar things—without an input form—not only with variables but with entire directories, too.)

Play around with the Variable Browser, as you wish—and read more about it in your HP User's Guide.

The Recovery Commands

There are four operations that can:

- Save you time
- Save you grief from errors

$\boxed{\rightarrow}\boxed{\text{CMD}}$

The 48 saves the last *four* most recently entered Command Lines in a special part of its memory—just in case you need to retrieve a long, hairy Command Line, make one small change, and re-enter it.

Example: Create these algebraics:

(a) $'-\int((X+6)/(X^2-5))+X^2'$

(b) $'\int(X^3-8)'$

(c) $'\int((X+6)/(X^2+5))-X^2'$

Solution: $\boxed{'}\boxed{+/-}\boxed{\sqrt{x}}\boxed{\leftarrow}\boxed{()}\boxed{\leftarrow}\boxed{()}\boxed{\alpha}\boxed{X}\boxed{+}\boxed{6}\boxed{\blacktriangleright}\boxed{\div}\boxed{\leftarrow}\boxed{()}\boxed{\alpha}\boxed{X}\boxed{y^x}\boxed{2}\boxed{-}\boxed{5}\boxed{\blacktriangleright}$
$\boxed{\blacktriangleright}\boxed{+}\boxed{\alpha}\boxed{X}\boxed{y^x}\boxed{2}\boxed{\text{ENTER}}\ \boxed{'}\boxed{\sqrt{x}}\boxed{\leftarrow}\boxed{()}\boxed{\alpha}\boxed{X}\boxed{y^x}\boxed{3}\boxed{-}\boxed{8}\boxed{\text{ENTER}}$
$\boxed{\rightarrow}\boxed{\text{CMD}}\boxed{\blacktriangledown}\boxed{\text{ENTER}}$
$\boxed{\rightarrow}\boxed{\text{ENTRY}}\boxed{\rightarrow}\boxed{\text{ENTRY}}\boxed{\rightarrow}\boxed{\blacktriangleright}\boxed{\blacktriangleleft}\boxed{\blacktriangleleft}\boxed{\blacktriangleleft}\boxed{\blacktriangleleft}\boxed{\leftarrow}\boxed{-}\boxed{\blacktriangleleft}\boxed{\blacktriangleleft}\boxed{\blacktriangleleft}\boxed{\blacktriangleleft}\boxed{\leftarrow}\boxed{+}\boxed{\text{ENTER}}$

$\boxed{\rightarrow}\boxed{\text{CMD}}$ offers you a CHOOS box of the four most recent Command Lines.

Try This: Assuming the three algebraics from the previous example are still on the Stack, press ⊞ to add two of them. Oops...you didn't really want to do that. Now what? How can you recover from such an error?

Solution: Use ⟶UNDO to retrieve the Stack as it was *before the most recent command* (that was ⊞ here).

Calculate: $(4 \times 5) + 4^5 - (4 + 5)$

Solution: 4 ENTER 5 ✕ ⟶ARG y^x ⟶ARG ⊞ ⊟ ⊞.
Result (FIX 3): **1,035.000**   ⟶ARG returns all of the arguments consumed by the last command.

Another: Evaluate $\sqrt{\dfrac{1+x}{x^2+7}} - x$, for $x = 3$. Then press ⟶ARG.

Solution: ⟵EQUATION $\sqrt{x}$ ▲ 1 ⊞ α X ▼ α X y^x 2 ▶ ⊞ 7 ▶ ▶ ⊟ α X
ENTER 3 ' α X STO EVAL ⟶ARG ....   Results:
-2.500 (Level3)   **0.500** (Level2)   **3.000** (Level1)
The arguments of ⊟, *the last command in the expression*, return to the Stack (the radical evaluates to **0.500**).

218

Often, switching back to a previous menu involves only one or two keystrokes, in which case →MENU is no shortcut. But to switch easily to the back "pages" of a menu—or into the interior of a nested set of menus, →MENU is a lifesaver.

To Wit: 2.351 Å/sec + 4.56 μ/min = __??__ m/yr

Solution: 2 · 3 5 1 →UNITS **LENG** ←PREV **A**
                  →UNITS **TIME** → **S**
                  4 · 5 6 →MENU **μ** →MENU → **MIN** +
                  1 →MENU NXT **M** →MENU → **YR**
                  ←UNITS **CONV** ....

               Result: 2.406_m/yr

Customizing Your Workspace

Keyboard shortcuts are handy, but they can't do it all for you. Customizing your workspace can also go a long way toward reducing your keystrokes and headaches.

But before you leap into it, remember one caveat:

Customization should make you more organized, not less.

As obvious as this advice seems, it's quite easy to get lost in the levels of customizing options that 48 provides—so that you end up making more work for yourself.

Briefly then, here are some specific ways you *can* customize your 48:

- Organize your workspace into *directories*.
- Create custom *menus*.
- Create custom *keyboard layouts*.
- Create custom *flag setups* (mode settings).
- Create custom *tools*.

How much of this customizing you *should* do depends on your needs. The remainder of this chapter is devoted to introducing you to these customization approaches and how they best fit together into an optimization approach.

Directory Structure

You've dealt with directories briefly in this Course, but here's a more "full-blown" scenario to consider: Assume for a moment that you're an engineering student with a wide range of basic problems and subjects in your courses. Therefore, the most important organizational decision you make on your 48 is probably your directory structure.

One option is simply to use your **HOME** directory for everything. To see where this gets you, take a look at your **HOME** VAR menu right now. If you've done all the examples and problems in this book, that menu now has nearly *twenty* pages. You'll wear out your NXT key (and your patience) looking for any given VARiable if you insist on dumping everything in your **HOME** directory. Not only that, you'll be limited to keeping only *one* variable named '**Y**' or '**X**' at a time—despite the vast numbers of equations that use these common variable names.

A better option is to subdivide your work into a structure of meaningful groups and subgroups. After careful thought, you—the engineering student—might come up with something like this:

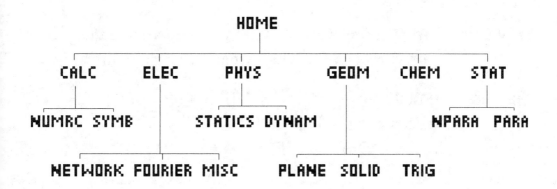

Do It: Create that directory structure and return to **HOME** directory.

Go: `'` `α` `α` `C` `A` `L` `C` `α` `⇐MEMORY` `DIR` `CRDIR`

`'` `α` `α` `E` `L` `E` `C` `α` `CRDIR`   `'` `α` `α` `P` `H` `Y` `S` `α` `CRDIR`

`'` `α` `α` `G` `E` `O` `M` `α` `CRDIR`   `'` `α` `α` `C` `H` `E` `M` `α` `CRDIR`

`'` `α` `α` `S` `T` `A` `T` `α` `CRDIR`

`VAR` `STAT` `'` `α` `α` `N` `P` `A` `R` `A` `α` `⇨MENU` `CRDIR`

`'` `α` `α` `P` `A` `R` `A` `α` `CRDIR`

`⇨HOME` `VAR` `GEOM` `'` `α` `α` `P` `L` `A` `N` `E` `α` `⇨MENU` `CRDIR`

`'` `α` `α` `S` `O` `L` `I` `D` `α` `CRDIR` `'` `α` `α` `T` `R` `I` `G` `α` `CRDIR`

`⇨HOME` `VAR` `PHYS` `'` `α` `α` `S` `T` `A` `T` `I` `C` `S` `α` `⇨MENU` `CRDIR`

`'` `α` `α` `D` `Y` `N` `A` `M` `α` `CRDIR`

`⇨HOME` `VAR` `ELEC` `'` `α` `α` `N` `E` `T` `W` `O` `R` `K` `α` `⇨MENU` `CRDIR`

`'` `α` `α` `F` `O` `U` `R` `I` `E` `R` `α` `CRDIR` `'` `α` `α` `M` `I` `S` `C` `α` `CRDIR`

`⇨HOME` `VAR` `CALC` `'` `α` `α` `N` `U` `M` `R` `C` `α` `⇨MENU` `CRDIR`

`'` `α` `α` `S` `Y` `M` `B` `α` `CRDIR` `⇨HOME` `VAR`.

Now you can tidy up your **HOME** directory's VAR menu, by PURGing the unwanted variables and moving those that you do want to keep.

Tidy Up: Write a program, MOVV, to move a variable to another directory and PURGE it from the original directory.

Like So: MOVV: « → a b « PATH a DUP
RCL SWAP b EVAL STO
EVAL a PURGE » »

---

⑤ *Customizing Your Workshop*

MOVV expects the *name* of the object on Level 2 and the PATH list of the target subdirectory at Level 1 of the Stack. For example, to move the variable 'EXPR' to the NUMRC subdirectory of CALC, you would press ⊡ EXPR (in the VAR menu) ENTER, and ⇦ {} ⇨ HOME α α C A L C SPC N U M R C ENTER, and VAR MOVV. To see your results, you would then press NXT CALC NUMR; EXPR will be on that directory's menu.*

And: While you're at it, create a program, COPY, in your HOME directory, that copies a variable into another directory *without* purging it from its current directory.

$$\text{COPY: « → a b « PATH a DUP}$$
$$\text{RCL SWAP b EVAL STO}$$
$$\text{EVAL » »}$$

Use It: Use MOVV and COPY (and ⇦ PURGE) to shorten the VAR menu of your HOME directory to 2-3 pages. Most of those variables have been stored for this Easy Course and aren't going to be useful to you in the future, so you can purge them (save any you think you may use). When cleaning house, remember that ⇦ VIEW allows you to quickly view the variables on one menu page.

Notice also that HP has built in an entire application for viewing, moving, copying, and purging variables. Feel free to explore the ⇨ MEMORY menu on your own, as you wish.

---

*MOVV does not check to see if a VARiable of the same name is already stored in the target subdirectory. If so, you'll lose the contents of that VARiable when MOVV executes. Of course, you could modify MOVV so that it *does* check for a pre-existing VARiable by that name.

Custom Menus

Now that your directories are in place, it's time to make some *custom menus* that will serve you conveniently in your engineering student "career."

A menu is just a list of objects that the 48 associates with the menu keys and a menu display via the MENU command.

Watch: To go to the first page of the MODES menu, you could, of course, press ←[MODES]; *or* you could instead press [6][3][α][α] [M][E][N][U][ENTER].

The MENU command understands that a real number argument refers to a *built-in menu*. Most built-in menus have corresponding numbers (see Appendix C of your User's Guide).

Another: Go to *the third page* of the UNITS VOL menu.

Solution: [4][5][·][0][3][α][α][M][E][N][U][ENTER]. The page number of the menu is given by two digits after the decimal point (if none are given, the 48 assumes .01).

Notice that the CST (CuSTom) menu has the number 1. That is, the list of objects currently stored in the variable named CST *in the current directory* is assigned the menu number 1 by the 48.

This is your *custom* menu—custom because you can readily change the list stored in that VARiable CST. And keep in mind that:

- You can have a different CST VARiable in every directory;
- You can create many lists in a directory—lists that can be menu lists whenever you decide to store them into CST.

Try One: Move to the ❴ HOME CALC SYMB ❵ directory and create a custom menu containing the functions COLCT, EXPAN, ISOL, →Qπ, and two short programs, PRINC and GEN that set and clear flag −1, respectively.

OK: [VAR][NXT] [CALC] [SYMB].

Then: [←][«] [»][1][+/−][SPC][α][S][α][F][ENTER]
['][α][α][P][R][I][N][C] [ENTER][STO][←][«] [»]
[1][+/−][SPC][α][C][α][F][ENTER]['][α][α][G][E][N][ENTER][STO].
These will appear on the VAR menu in the SYMB directory.

Next, create the menu list and store it into CST: [←][❴❵]
[←][SYMBOLIC] [COLCT] [EXPA] [ISOL] [NXT] [→Qπ] [→][MENU]
[GEN] [PRINC] [ENTER]['][α][α][C][S][T][ENTER][STO].

Now test it—press [CST]. Presto!

Now go back to the **HOME** directory ([→][HOME]) to see what custom menu you get.... It's probably blank (if you don't have anything stored into **CST** at the **HOME** level yet) or it's some other menu. But no matter what, *this is not the same menu you just created.* That one is available only when you're in the **SYMB** subdirectory.

Now, the thought may occur to you that this list could be useful as a custom menu in several of your engineering directories. So, should you copy the list to the **CST** VARiables in the other directories?

Probably not. There's only one **CST** in each directory and you don't want to monopolize all of them with copies of the same menu. A better approach is to store that particular menu list into some other name, and make it available to all of the directories, so that when you need it, you can store *its name* into the **CST** variable at that time.

Try It: Move to the **SYMB** subdirectory again and retrieve the list stored in **CST**. Name it **CALG** and store it as a variable in the **HOME** directory—so that it's accessible to all directories (remember how directory paths work?).

Simple: [VAR][NXT] **CALC** **SYMB** **CST** [→][HOME] ['][α][α][C][A][L][G][ENTER] [STO]. Now, from any directory, you need only to store the name **CALG** into the local **CST** variable (either with [STO] or with the MENU command), and then press [CST] to activate your custom menu.*

---

*Note, incidentally, that when you use [CST], if the name **CST** is not defined in the current directory, the 48 will use **CST** from the parent directory.

Actually, you really ought to name all of your custom menu lists. This allows you to switch easily between different custom menus.

Some—like CALG—may be useful for many directories and therefore you store them in the **HOME** directory so that they're accessible by all. But if you have other menu lists whose uses are more specific to a given directory, you would store those list names there. The point is—as with any VARiable—you control the universality of access to a custom menu list by where you store it.

Keep in mind, too, that even if the 48 can find your custom menu list name to store into CST, this doesn't guarantee that it will be able to find the *menu items* named in that list.

Try This: At **HOME**, press ⎡'⎤ CALG ENTER ⎡'⎤ α α C S T α STO CST
PRINC.... What happens? Instead of executing PRINC (i.e. setting flag −1), you get the empty name, 'PRINC'. The 48 can't find any object associated with that name.

Of course not—the VARiable, PRINC, is stored *down* the hierarchy in the ❴ HOME CALC SYMB ❵ directory. That's not in the PATH of the **HOME** directory, so it's currently invisible to the 48. So use MOVV to move PRINC and GEN back to the **HOME** directory where they now belong.

No matter how you invoke it (by typing it or via a VAR menu or custom menu), a VARiable name can be evaluated only if it's in the current PATH.

Custom menus work much like the built-in menus—including (STO) and (RCL) for (←) and (→)—unless you have other uses for the shift keys....

Example: Modify CALG so that instead of using three menu keys for COLCT, EXPAN, and ISOL, you use just one. Make COLCT the normal (unshifted) choice, EXPAN the left-shifted ((←)) choice and ISOL the right-shifted ((→)) choice.

Solution: Create this list: { { "C, E, I" { COLCT EXPAN ISOL } } →Qπ GEN PRINC }

Note the format for each item with shifted meanings: { "*item name*" { action (←)-action (→)-action } }

This list-within-a-list appears wherever you wish it to appear (first position in this case) in the custom menu. Store this list in CALG (at **HOME**), and use (CST) to test it.

This is how to pack more functionality onto six menu keys. Of course, your custom menus can have multiple pages, too—but after a couple of pages, you'd be playing hide-and-seek again with all the choices.

Do This: Turn CALG into a one-stop custom menu packed with useful goodies gathered from various built-in menus:

Item name	C,E,I	MISC	DRG	FLG	DIGIT	STAK
Normal	COLCT	1_m	DEG	FS?	FIX	ROLL
Left-shifted	EXPAN	1_ft	RAD	SF	STD	ROLLD
Right-shifted	ISOL	IFTE	GRAD	CF	RND	PICK

Solution: Store this list as CALG in the **HOME** directory:

```
{ { "C,E,I" { COLCT EXPAN ISOL } }
{ "MISC" { 1_m 1_ft IFTE } }
{ "DRG" { DEG RAD GRAD } }
{ "FLG" { FS? SF CF } }
{ "DIGIT" { FIX STD RND } }
{ "STAK" { ROLL ROLLD PICK } } }
```

CALG is now a very useful custom menu list, so useful, in fact, you might want it available any time—without overwriting the CST in the current directory. That is, you might want CALG as a *temporary* custom menu:

Look: « CALG TMENU », stored as CMEN in your **HOME** directory, lets you use CALG *without putting it into* CST. You invoke a *temporary* menu with the TMENU command. Like any other menu, it remains active until another menu replaces it. It's just a custom menu that doesn't use any CST VARiable.

Custom Keyboards

With custom menus, you redefine the menu keys—including their shifted versions. But what about the rest of the keys on the keyboard? HP has laid out the keyboard on the 48 to make it maximally useful for most people. But in case you're not "most people" or in case you have a special program or application, HP has also made it possible to totally "redo" the keyboard.

In fact, you may have already seen examples of this: Whenever you enter a special environment—such as the Equation Writer—the keyboard is reassigned. Only a few of the keys are functional and their operations change to fit the special needs of the environment.

It's done like this: Each and every physical key is identified by its row and column numbers. The (VAR) key is 24 because it's the fourth key in the second row. Similarly, (ENTER) is 51; (yˣ) is 45; (3) is 84; (◄) is 55, etc.

Then, each physical key location has up to six standard definitions—corresponding with its six shift positions (recall page 28). For example, key location 73 ((5)) has the following six definitions:

1 Unshifted ((5)):   the number 5
2 Left-shifted ((←)(STAT)):   page one of the STAT menu.
3 Right-shifted ((→)(STAT)):   the STAT application.
4 Alpha ((α)(STAT)):   the character "5"
5 Alpha left-shifted ((α)(←)(STAT)): the character "£"
6 Alpha right-shifted ((α)(→)(STAT)): the character "¥"

Plus, *you* can assign to each key location up to six more definitions (*user-assigned* definitions), which become active whenever the 48 is in User mode. Thus a physical key location may have up to twelve definitions assigned to it—six built-in (active in normal mode) and six user-assigned (active in User Mode).

To make a key assignment, you assign an object to a key number. For example, in the standard (built-in) keyboard definitions, the character "£" is assigned to the key 73.5, where the 73 is the key location and the .5 indicates which shift position. The codes for the shift positions correspond to the list above—except that the unshifted position is designated by either .1 or .0 (or no digit at all).

Try It: Change ⬅️⟶NUM so that it executes ⇥Q𝜋 instead.

Easy: Enter the object: ⬅️« »⬅️SYMBOLIC NXT ⇥Q𝜋 ENTER
Enter the desired location and shift mode: 3 3 • 2 ENTER
Assign the key: ⬅️MODES KEYS ASN .

Then, you access User mode much the same as you do alpha mode: Press ⬅️USR once and your keyboard is the user keyboard for just the next keystroke. Press ⬅️USR ⬅️USR and you're in User mode until you press ⬅️USR a third time.

Try both now, and test your key assignment....

You can *change* your custom keyboard, too: Just as the current custom menu refers to a *list* named or stored in CST, so the current custom keyboard refers to a *list* of key assignments stored in memory.

Look: Press RCLK to retrieve the current user keyboard list.

Result (STD mode): { S « →Qπ » 33.2 }. The S means that the user keyboard is the same as the Standard keyboard *except* for the items following it in the list (i.e. with no key assignments at all, RCLK would yield simply { S }).

That means that you can use named lists to store and save special keyboard settings—ready to "install" them when you need them.

Example: Redefine these keys to produce audio tones at specified intervals in the musical scale, given a starting pitch:*

Key	Interval (half-steps)	Key	Interval (half-steps)
ENTER	0		
▼	−1	←▼	−12
▲	+1	→▲	+12
◄	−2		
►	+2		

*A complete-octave musical scale is a geometric series of 12 audio frequencies, called half-steps. The 13th frequency is the octave—*double* the frequency of the first.

Solution: First, a little program to compute and sound the correct interval (for 1 second), given a starting frequency:

```
INTV: « 2 12 INV ^ SWAP ^
      * DUP 1 BEEP »
```

Store this in **HOME**. Then, here's the key assignment list:

```
{ S « 0 INTV » 51
    « -1 INTV » 35 « -12 INTV » 35.2
    « 1 INTV » 25 « 12 INTV » 25.3
    « -2 INTV » 34 « 2 INTV » 36 }
```

Store this list as TONES in **HOME**, and then make it your User keyboard: (VAR)**TONE** (←)(MODES)**KEYS STOK**.

Now test it: Key in a starting frequency, (4)(4)(0)(ENTER), then press (←)(USR)(←)(USR) and horse around with (ENTER) and the arrow keys.*

The point here is that you have saved these key assignments in the list named **TONES**, so you can reinstate them any time you want.

---

*Notice how it helps to use the existing labels of the keys: If your assignments are at all similar to keyboard functions, consider locating them there (as did the example on the previous page). If that isn't practicable, and if you use a lot of key assignments so that it isn't convenient to try to memorize what and where they are, you might consider plastic keyboard overlays (available from HP and/or their dealers). Notice also that although reassigning the (ENTER) key is certainly allowable, it's not too wise. After all, it's one of the most heavily used keys; if you need it—as (ENTER)—along with your key assignments, you'll find yourself constantly having to toggle in and out of **USER** mode. Not so handy.

You'll notice that the other keys still retain their standard definitions while you're in **USER** mode. Can you disable them so that only your reassigned keys work?

Sure: Just delete the standard key definitions, S: ⬅️USR❩'⟮α⟯⟮S⟯ENTER ⬅️MODES KEYS DELK . Now press RCLK to see the current user key assignments.... The S is gone.

But: Notice also that →Qπ is still defined as the ⬅️→NUM key. How can that be? When you assigned TONES via STOK , didn't that wipe out the previous custom keyboard?

No: Custom *menus* use a VARiable (CST) to store the current menu list, so storing a new list into CST does indeed *replace* the previous custom menu. However, custom key assignments are stored in a reserved part of memory, and storing new key assignments *add* to the previous key assignments; only the specific keys designated in the new list get their assignments replaced. You must specifically delete any old key assignments that you don't want.

Do It: Delete the →Qπ user key assignment.

OK: Press ③③•② **DELK**. Confirm your work with **RCLK**.*

Finally, what if you now need some of the standard keys—say, (ENTER), (←), (CST), (VAR), and the menu keys? How do you restore their standard definitions without restoring all of the standard keys?

Easy: Simply assign the name, 'SKEY', to each standard key you want to restore. Here's the list:

{ SKEY 51 SKEY 55 SKEY 23 SKEY 24 SKEY
11 SKEY 12 SKEY 13 SKEY 14 SKEY 15 SKEY 16 }

Store these additional user key assignments: **STOK**.

You now have a user keyboard where only some keys have definitions. Whenever you press a key that has no current definition, you'll hear the error beep to let you know that it's "dead."

---

*"Old", deleted key assignments still take up memory unless you periodically *repack* the way they're stored. This sequence accomplishes the repacking: **RCLK** ⓪ **DELK** **STOK**. If you use custom keyboards often, you should repack your keyboard memory regularly.

Custom Flag Settings

You know how to set and clear flags individually with ■ᎦF■ and ■CF■. Also, for some system flags (such as –3), you can use the special menu items (■ᎦᎽᎷ◻■) to toggle between set and clear. And here is a more in-depth reminder how, like the user-key assignments, you can store and recall a list of all the flag settings and save that list as a VARiable for later use.

Do This: Press ⬅(MODES) ■FLAG■ (NXT) ■RCLF■. You'll get a list of two binary integer objects (recall page 105). The first integer shows the states of all system flags (from –1 to –64); the second one shows the states of the user flags (from 1 to 64). Store this list as a variable, OLDF: ⌐(α)(α)(O)(L)(D)(F)(α)(STO).

Now change some flags: (NXT)(6)(4)(+/–) ■ᎦF■ ⬅(MODES) ■FMT■ (3) ■FIX■ ⬅(MODES) ■MISC■ ■ᎦᎽᎷ◻■ ⬅(MODES) ■ANGL■ ■RAD■ (MTH) ■BASE■ ■BIN■. Recall the new flag settings: (NXT)(6)(4) ■STWS■ ⬅(MODES) ■FLAG■ (NXT) ■RCLF■.

In binary format, you can see (use ⬅(EDIT) to explore) the 64 bits corresponding to the states of the 64 system flags:*

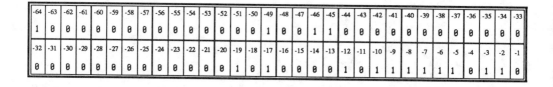

-64	-63	-62	-61	-60	-59	-58	-57	-56	-55	-54	-53	-52	-51	-50	-49	-48	-47	-46	-45	-44	-43	-42	-41	-40	-39	-38	-37	-36	-35	-34	-33
1	0	0	0	0	0	0	0	0	0	0	0	0	0	0	0	1	0	0	1	1	0	0	0	0	0	0	0	0	0	0	0

-32	-31	-30	-29	-28	-27	-26	-25	-24	-23	-22	-21	-20	-19	-18	-17	-16	-15	-14	-13	-12	-11	-10	-9	-8	-7	-6	-5	-4	-3	-2	-1
0	0	0	0	0	0	0	0	0	0	0	0	0	1	0	1	0	0	0	0	1	0	1	1	1	1	1	1	1	0	1	1

---

*You might have flags cleared or set other than the ones shown here. You may wish to refer to Appendix D of your User's Guide to confirm what each flag indicates in its current state.

Notice that the user flag integer (the second value) isn't 64 bits long. The 48 doesn't display leading zeroes in its binary integers, so the binary format of the integer representing flag conditions will be only as long as the number of highest *set* flag (i.e. the left-most 1).*

To demonstrate this, clear flag –64 and press `RCLK` once again.... The result is only 50 bits long; all flags numbered above –50 are clear (0).

Now: You could, of course, store this list for later retrieval too—but don't bother. Suppose, however, that you do want to restore the original flag settings as saved in the list VARiable, OLDF.

Easy: `VAR` `OLDF` `←` `MODES` `FLAG` `NXT` `STOF`.

So if you're using some program that requires a certain combination of system flag states, this is how to quickly set all those states—and preserve the previous flag states, too (so that you don't mess things up for the next task).

*You'll get all 64 bits only if flags –5 through –10 are set. That's the 64-bit default setting for the wordsize—recall page 103.

Optimization: A Case Study

All right, you've seen certain hypothetical examples of lists that allow you to customize your calculator. Now, how will *you* use such ideas to save yourself labor and trouble?

First, go back to your original directory structure. Ask yourself which directories might benefit from custom menus or custom keyboards. If you find some likely candidates, build and store the custom lists for these goodies in the appropriate directories. And if there some custom lists—like CALG—that should be available more generally, put them in the HOME directory.

Next, refine the structure of your VAR menus by adding small touches.

For example, imagine that you're creating a VAR menu for your directory, { HOME PHYS DYNAM }. When you select DYNM to enter that directory, you'll see its VAR menu.

What do you want in this menu? It's worth a little thought....

Suppose: You want a custom menu, MEN1, to use with your motion calculations—plus you want CALG available, too. Then you'd like to be able to push one key to set the flags and user keyboard for the kind of work you do in this directory—and another key to reset the flags and keys as they were before, when you've finished. And suppose you want these features always to appear on the *first* page of your VAR menu. How are you going to do all this?

Well: Here's one approach (you may think of others): First, in your DYNAM directory, create and name the programs that handle the various customizing details:

SET1: « RCLF 'OLDF' STO RCLKEYS 'OLDK' STO
        CFL1 STOF 0 DELKEYS CKY1 STOKEYS
        CPP1 'PPAR' STO CΣP1 'ΣPAR' STO »

MEN1: « CMN1 MENU »

ALGM: « CALG TMENU »

QUIT: « 0 DELKEYS OLDK STOKEYS OLDF STOF
        HOME 2 MENU »

Next, create and name your custom lists:

CMN1: { the items you want in your custom menu }
CFL1: { #system flags value #user flags value }
CKY1: { your custom key assignments }
CPP1: { your custom plotting parameters }
CΣP1: { your custom statistical parameters }

Finally, use the ORDER function to specify that SET1, MEN1, ALGM, and QUIT all appear on the first page of the VAR menu. Create a list of the names you want placed:

$$\{ \ SET1 \ \ MEN1 \ \ ALGM \ \ QUIT \ \}$$

Then press ←(MEMORY) DIR ORDER. Now anything not included in this list will be placed after these items.

Now your keystrokes are fairly well streamlined: As an engineering student, to get started with the dynamics problems in your physics class, starting at HOME, you would press PHYS DYNA, then SET1 to configure your flags, keyboard and analysis parameters. At that point, you're ready to start on the problems themselves. You have all of your calculation variables available via (VAR) and your optimized menus via MEN1 or (CST) or ALGM.

That's doing *a lot* in very few keystrokes. And you can use this same basic idea and structure in your other directories, too—even using the same names of variables and custom lists, if the consistency helps. Notice the naming scheme for your customized lists. If you found yourself later needing, say, two different plotting parameter setups in the course of your analyses, you could name a second list CPP2, right?

Putting It All Together

The 48 workshop isn't difficult to learn how to use, but it's a real challenge is to choose appropriately among its myriad options for tools and methods. Only you can decide what parts are of interest to you; nobody uses it all. Consider the possibilities as you take this final quiz....

Custom Questions

1. When and why might you not be able to use the recovery keys?

2. How do these storage commands differ? STO STOKEYS STOF

3. What binary integer represents the default system flag states— the flag states as they would be after a system reset? (Don't do this—just think about it.)

4. As an engineering student, suppose that you do a large number of rigid-free-body analysis problems. You input vectors corresponding to forces, positions and moments acting on the body and then calculate the resultant sums of the forces and moments. You also do a great deal of "what-iffing," so you need to be able to store, retrieve, and edit specific descriptions for specific bodies. What strategy might you use to do all this on your 48?

Optimum Answers

1. (UNDO), (ARG), (CMD), and (MENU) all allow you to recover information
    after you've moved on. But keeping these hidden records costs
    memory, and if you prefer not to spend that memory on such
    recovery features, you can so specify. (MENU) is one of the built-in
    menu numbers (0); you can't turn this feature off. But you can
    control (ARG) via a toggle key in the MODES MISC menu. And also
    in the MODES MISC menu are the toggle keys for disabling (CMD)
    and (UNDO) (the latter via the ▉▇▓▉ key). These two features can
    use a lot of memory; if you need more memory, these might be the
    first ones to forego, if appropriate.

2. Of these three, only STO allows you to control where in user
    memory (i.e. directory structure) you are storing an object: STO
    stores an object into the given name in the current VAR menu,
    overwriting the object (if any) previously stored there. STOKEYS
    stores a list of user key assignments into an unnamed place in the
    48 memory. This overwrites the previous key assign-ments only
    for the specific keys in the given argument list, leaving all other
    key assignments intact. STOF stores a binary integer (or list of
    two binary integers) into an unnamed place in the 48's memory.
    Each integer affects *all* of its 64 flags.

3. In the default settings, only flags −5 through −10 are set (for a
    binary wordsize of 64). This value is # 1111110000b (which is
    # 3F0h or # 1012d).

242

4. First, you'd probably want to set up some custom configurations in your 𝗦𝗧𝗔𝗧𝗜𝗖𝗦 directory—similar to the approach you saw on pages 238-240.

In your flags, for example, you might want to clear flag −19 (so that you can build vectors rather than complex numbers with the ⟵[2D] and [→][3D] keys) and set, say, ENG 2 display mode, then DEGrees for angles, and probably cylindrical vector mode.

As for your custom menu, before you can set that up, you need to envision the calculations themselves. For example, how are you going to build a complete description of each free body—with all its forces and moments acting upon it—into a single object that you can then name (FB1, FB2, etc.) for storage and use later? A *list* of some kind would do it, right?

Then what objects would be included in each body-description list? Vectors, probably, but how will you distinguish force vectors —with their corresponding position vectors—from moment vectors, which need no positional information? How about three lists of vectors? The first two (forces and positions) would have the same number of vectors in them and correspond one-for-one; the third list would contain all the moment vectors.

Then you might want to build yourself some little editing tools—to make it easier to input, alter, delete and view the vectors in each of the lists. Such items would indeed be handy on your custom menu. And, of course, you'll need the calculation routines themselves—the summation of the forces and the summation of the moments—also good candidates for your custom menu.

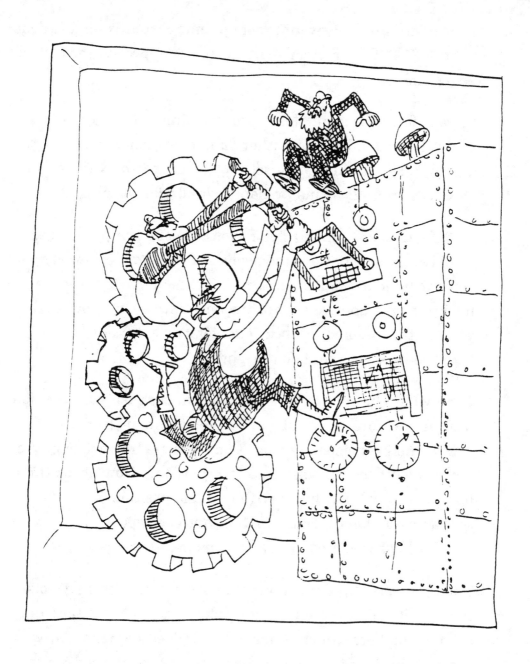

6 PROGRAMMING PRACTICE

Before You Study

In previous chapters, you've seen some "nuts and bolts" of programming the HP 48. You now know something about local variables, conditional tests, loops, custom menus, key assignments and directories. But that doesn't automatically make you a programmer. If someone hands you a box of machine parts, that doesn't necessarily mean you know how to put them together to get a properly working mechanism.

So in this final chapter you'll see some examples of programming the HP 48—plus some ideas for a variety of interesting tasks that you can pursue further on your own. Hopefully, you'll come away with a feel for the power and possibilities of the HP 48. It is loaded with sophisticated commands, but often it's hard to grasp their significance until you envision a task where they would come in handy. These examples were selected for their ability to show a variety of machine features. So at least browse through them to see what various commands can do.

One thing to reassure yourself right now: No matter how experienced you become, programming is never a tidy, straightforward science. The programs shown here didn't just pop out onto the pages in final form. They evolved out of many strategy changes, coding mistakes and a lot of "horsing around." The whole idea of writing a program is to build a useful new tool from the tools already available. But it will take you a few iterations to discover exactly what is most useful—and most appropriate, given the time you have, the purpose of the program, and capabilities (and limitations) of the HP 48. Get used to this iteration process; it never goes away entirely (and besides, it's where you do the most learning). With more proficiency, you will simply iterate more quickly and easily toward an appropriate solution.

One other reminder: The programs in this chapter use certain conventions—not requirements, but recommended *habits* that will help you if you adopt them in your own programming:

- Every program is listed with a checksum after its name, to help you catch typing errors. For example: Ft→FIS (# 40362d)

  To obtain the checksum (and memory usage) of any object, store the object in its intended *Name*, then type 'Name' BYTES. The first output returned (in Level 2) is the checksum—shown as a binary integer in the current binary format (binary word size: 64). The second output (in Level 1) is the memory usage of the object.

- Every program is listed in expanded, indented form, with comments, so that you can clearly trace what's going on and keep the sub-modules (« »), loops, branches, and tests straight. Just ignore these line breaks when actually keying in the code.

- To modify an existing program, you generally use the keystrokes 'Name' ENTER, ←EDIT, *modifying keystrokes*, ENTER. (Note that the HP 48's presentation of a program in EDIT mode is different than the expanded, indented form mentioned above.)

- All local variables are entirely in lowercase; all global variables are capitalized (but not entirely in uppercase). This helps you see more clearly in a listing exactly what is local, what is global and what is built-in (which is generally all uppercase). Thus, for example, p would be a local variable, Purge would be global, and PURGE is, of course, the built-in command. Keep in mind, too, that on a menu, all characters *appear* uppercase, but they aren't necessarily so.

A Calculator of Feet, Inches, and Sixteenths

This first topic is a case study—a comparison of various strategies to solve a problem. You may be familiar with how the HP 48 can format a time or angle—in minutes and seconds—as one number: *hh.mmss* Thus, for example, 135°42'9" is formatted as 135.4209. And 2:15:36 p.m. is formatted as 14.1536. But there are other notations that aren't quite "decimal" format either. One such notation is feet, inches and sixteenths of inches ("FIS"). This case study is a simple set of arithmetic and trigonometry solutions for problems that use this notation.

Challenge: In the HOME directory, create a new directory called FIS. Then, in FIS, write two programs, Ft→FIS and FIS→Ft, to convert between decimal feet and FIS notation.

Solutions: Ft→FIS (# 40362d)

```
«
   9 RND DUP IP
   SWAP FP
   12 *
   9 RND
   DUP IP
   SWAP FP .16 *
   +
   .01 * +
»
```

Eliminate re-conversion round-off error in whole feet; get whole feet and fraction.
Get whole inches and eliminate re-conversion roundoff error there, too.
Get sixteenths.
Build formatted number from its three parts.

FIS→Ft (# 56872d)

```
«
   DUP IP
   SWAP FP 100 * DUP
   IP 12 /
   SWAP FP 100 * 192 /
   + +
»
```

Get whole feet.
Get inches & sixteenths.
Convert whole inches.
Convert sixteenths.
Find decimal sum.

Notice, then, that with those two routines, you can easily create other conversions to/from FIS, by using the units features of the HP 48.

Challenge: Write a pair of programs, M→FIS and FIS→M, to convert between meters and FIS.

Solutions: M→FIS (# 16016d)

```
«
    1_m  →UNIT       Create unit (in meters) from value.
    1_ft CONVERT     Convert to equivalent in feet.
    UVAL Ft→FIS      Convert value portion to FIS.
»
```

FIS→M (# 47621d)

```
«
    FIS→Ft           Convert value to decimal feet.
    1_ft →UNIT       Create unit (in feet) from value.
    1_m CONVERT      Convert to equivalent in meters.
    UVAL             Keep value portion only.
»
```

Of course, you could do similar conversions to/from any other units of length, as well. The point here is how easily any tool—whether built-in or created by you—can then become a part in another tool. You'll be using FIS→Ft and Ft→FIS often in the set of solutions you're now considering.

Reminder: Put all such FIS solutions in the FIS directory.

Now, many fabrications (welding, sheet metal) industries still use FIS in their length specifications, so they often need to do simple arithmetic in that notation. It would be very handy, therefore, to be able to add or subtract lengths, and to multiply/divide lengths by scalars.

Challenge: Write four small programs, FISA, FISS, FISSM and FISD, that add, subtract, multiply and divide, respectively, lengths in FIS format. For FISM and FISD, assume that the second argument is a scalar, not a length.

Solutions:

FISA (# 25401d)
```
«
    FIS→Ft SWAP FIS→Ft     Convert both arguments
    + Ft→FIS               to decimal feet; sum;
»                          convert result to FIS.
```

FISS (# 51896d)
```
«
    NEG FISA               Just negate second argu-
»                          ment, then add.
```

FISM (# 7028d)
```
«
    SWAP FIS→Ft *          Convert first argument
    Ft→FIS                 (second is scalar); multi-
»                          ply; reconvert to FIS.
```

FISD (# 39225d)
```
«
    INV FISM               Just invert second argu-
»                          ment, then multiply.
```

These are fairly straightforward. Notice how FISS uses FISA, and FISD uses FISM.

Also common in such industries is the need to calculate various right-triangle relations in FIS. That is, they often need to compute one of the following values, based upon two of the other three:

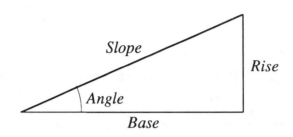

Value desired	Known values	Relation
Angle	*Base, Rise*	$Angle = \tan^{-1}(Rise \div Base)$
Angle	*Base, Slope*	$Angle = \cos^{-1}(Base \div Slope)$
Angle	*Rise, Slope*	$Angle = \sin^{-1}(Rise \div Slope)$
Base	*Angle, Rise*	$Base = Rise \div \tan(Angle)$
Base	*Angle, Slope*	$Base = Slope \bullet \cos(Angle)$
Base	*Rise, Slope*	$Base = \sqrt{(Slope^2 - Rise^2)}$
Rise	*Angle, Base*	$Rise = Base \bullet \tan(Angle)$
Rise	*Angle, Slope*	$Rise = Slope \bullet \sin(Angle)$
Rise	*Base, Slope*	$Rise = \sqrt{(Slope^2 - Base^2)}$
Slope	*Angle, Base*	$Slope = Base \div \cos(Angle)$
Slope	*Angle, Rise*	$Slope = Rise \div \sin(Angle)$
Slope	*Base, Rise*	$Slope = \sqrt{(Base^2 + Rise^2)}$

Project Challenge: Put all the various FIS tools together—conversions, arithmetic and the trig solutions shown opposite—in a convenient and logical manner.

You've already developed routines for the conversions and the arithmetic. The only questions remaining for those is where and how to make them available to the user.

The same is true for the trig solutions, also. The problem with those solutions is clearly not in the logic or the number-crunching within the programs; any given case is a simple calculation, mathematically. But with so many cases to allow for, the problem again becomes a question of how to offer those solutions *conveniently*.

Consider four different strategies....

Strategy 1: A Collection of Unconnected Programs

The first—and simplest—option is to write six small trig programs (and one small output utility)—enough to treat each possible combination of two trig unknowns. Just choose from among the relations shown on page 250, then store these alongside your FIS→Ft and Ft→FIS conversions and your arithmetic routines. For example:

```
A~BR (# 56621d)
   «
      Rise FIS→Ft Base FIS→Ft / ATAN
      'Angle' Out
   »
```

```
B~AR (# 10424d)
   «
      Rise FIS→Ft Angle TAN / Ft→FIS
      'Base' Out
   »
```

```
B~RS (# 52072d)
   «
      Slope FIS→Ft SQ Rise FIS→Ft SQ - √ Ft→FIS
      'Base' Out
   »
```

```
R~AS (# 29215d)
   «
      Angle SIN Slope FIS→Ft * Ft→FIS
      'Rise' Out
   »
```

```
R~BS (# 2815d)
   «
      Slope FIS→Ft SQ Base FIS→Ft SQ - √ Ft→FIS
      'Rise' Out
   »
```

S~AB (# 18158d)
«
    Base FIS→Ft Angle COS / Ft→FIS
    'Slope' Out
»

Out (# 55436d)
«
    DUP2 STO →TAG   *Duplicate value and name together; store*
»   *value; echo it with tagged Stack version.*

Notice how each formula simply carries out the respective trig relation as shown on page 250—after converting one or both known values form FIS to usable decimal form. Then, to present the output and restore the FIS format, each routine calls the Out routine, sending it not only the result value but the name of the variable that value represents.

Of course, this is definitely the "no-frills" strategy: For every calculation, you must find and select the correct program(s) from your VAR menu. With 6 trig and 4 arithmetic programs, you'll be using [NXT] and [←][PREV] a lot. Also, for your trig solutions, you'll sometimes need to run two trig programs to get your desired unknown from the available knowns (unless you wish to add the other 6 solutions as programs to your VAR menu and therefore have even more items to hunt through).

Notice, too, that you're assuming that Angle is in *decimal degrees*. To assume degrees, minutes and seconds, in each routine you'd insert →HR before using Angle as a known or →HMS after calculating it. And you must manually set DEG mode and the display format (4 FIX).

Strategy 2: Key Assignments and a List of SOLVR Formulas

With just a little work, you can relieve some of the "manual" aspects of the previous strategy. First of all, you could use a little setup program (to be undone by a cleanup program) to make some initial settings, assign the FIS arithmetic programs to arithmetic keys, and assign the conversion routines to, say, the [←][ENTER] and [EVAL] keys.

Secondly—in that same setup routine—you could cut down on the number and complexity of trig programs by asking the intelligence of the SOLVE application to do the actual math for you, via a linked list of equations. (Indeed, since you'll have two knowns in every equation, you can get away with a linked list of just three equations.) The SOLVR version of the SOLVE application is what to use, because it allows you to work in the Stack as well as in the application. That's what you need, since you'll want to see what you're doing with your arithmetic and conversion routines besides using the SOLVR menu.

The only catch is that a discrete quantity such as a FIS-formatted number doesn't work well in the SOLVE algorithm. So the trade-off is that you'll get more convenient trig solving, but you'll have to do your FIS/Ft conversions as separate steps—before and after the actual trig calculations—via your key assignments.

You may ask: "Why key assignments? Why not include the FIS conversion routines as part of a custom SOLVR menu?"

Good point. A *list*, describing a custom SOLVR *menu* (specifying the order of variables and including other executable programs) with the equation is allowable, *but only if it's a single equation*—not true here.

Setup (# 37067d)

```
«
    RCLF 'F' STO                          Save current flag states.
    RCLKEYS 'K' STO                       Save current key assignments.
    4 FIX DEG -62 SF                      Set displ., angle, USER modes.
    {
        Ft→FIS 33 FIS→Ft 51.2            List
        Cleanup 91.2                         of
        FISD 65 FISM 75                      key assignments
        FISS 85 FISA 95                      to be made.
    }
    STOKEYS                               Make the assignments.
    {
        'Angle=ATAN(Rise/Base)'          List of trig relation equations
        'Base=Slope*COS(Angle)'              to be rotated in and out
        'Rise=Slope*SIN(Angle)'              by the SOLVR.
    }
    STEQ                                  Store this list into EQ.
    75 MENU                               Get SOLVR ROOT menu.
»
```

Cleanup (# 63037d)   (Assigned to ◁CONT.)

```
«
    { 33 51.2 91.2 65 75 85 95 }         Delete key assign-
    DELKEYS                                  ments; restore
    K STOKEYS F STOF                         prev. keys, flags.
    { F K Angle Base Rise Slope EQ }     Purge unneeded
    PURGE                                    variables.
    HOME FIS 2 MENU                       Get VAR menu in
»                                             FIS directory.
```

To use this strategy, you would simply press **SETUP**, then press **SOLVR**
to start that application. Than you can use the arithmetic and trig
solutions as needed (keeping in mind that the SOLVR can handle only
decimal feet: FIS→Ft is on the ◁ENTER key and Ft→FIS is on the EVAL
key). Use **NXEQ** to find the equation whose unknown you must solve
for first.

When you're done, just press ◁CONT, and you've cleaned up!

Strategy 3: A Real MES

You can even dispense with the equation swapping needed within the SOLVR: the Multiple Equation Solver (MES) does it for you. This solution is almost identical to that of Strategy 2:

`Setup` (# 34247d)

```
«
    RCLF 'F' STO                        Save current flag states.
    RCLKEYS 'K' STO                     Save current key assignments.
    4 FIX DEG -62 SF                    Set displ., angle, USER modes.
    {
        Ft→FIS 33 FIS→Ft 51.2 Cleanup 91.2
        FISD 65 FISM 75 FISS 85 FISA 95
    }
    STOKEYS                             Make key assignments.
    {
        'Angle=ATAN(Rise/Base)'         List of trig relation equations
        'Base=Slope*COS(Angle)'            to be rotated in and out
        'Rise=Slope*SIN(Angle)'            by the SOLVR.
    }
    STEQ                                Store this list into EQ.
    MINIT MSOLVR                        Initialize MES, then get
»                                          its menu.
```

`Cleanup` (# 56236d)   *(Same as before except purge* Mpar, *too.)*

```
«
    { 33 51.2 91.2 65 75 85 95 } DELKEYS
    K STOKEYS F STOF
    { F K Angle Base Rise Slope EQ Mpar } PURGE
    HOME FIS 2 MENU
»
```

Press **SETUP**, and you're rolling. As before, use the arithmetic and trig solutions freely (with `FIS→Ft` on ⏴[ENTER] and `Ft→FIS` on [EVAL]). Note how the MES menu shows which variables you have defined (darkened) and which are consistent with the most recent solving (the ■'s).

Strategy 4: Your Own Personal MES

Admit it: You'd still love to have the Ultimate Solution—the equation-choosing smarts of the MES but with the convenience of a VAR menu and the ability to tolerate FIS formatting right in the variables—no conversions necessary on your part, either before and after the solving.

Well, you can do that: The setup program (call it &Go) would set angle and display settings and assign the arithmetic routines to the appropriate keys, as usual. It would assign Ft→FIS to the ←(ENTER) key—in case you ever have to deal with a length in decimal feet. (This is different than the previous solution where you had to use decimal feet for the SOLVR. Here, the entire process should accept FIS notation; the assignment of Ft→FIS to ←(ENTER) is only a just-in-case provision.)

Then &Go would create a custom menu containing your triangle parameters (**ANGL**, **BASE**, **RISE**, **SLOPE**)—a menu that *imitates the behavior pattern of your VAR menu:*

- Simply pressing a menu key *evaluates* (calculates) that variable based upon the current values of other variables;

- Pressing ←, then a menu key, *stores* a value (from Stack Level 1) into that variable;

- Pressing →, then a menu key, *recalls* that variable's value,

Also, this menu would offer a **CLEAR** key, which would set all variables to zero. As usual, the cleanup routine (call it Quit) would be assigned to the ←(CONT) key.

The calculation will be based upon which two variables were *modified* (either input or calculated) *most recently*. A history list (**Hist**) keeps track of this and is updated after every operation, in your **Out** routine.

Out (# 23851d)

```
«
    DUP ROT SWAP DUP2            Three copies of name, two of the value.
    STO →TAG SWAP                Store value; create Stack tag.
    → v                          Name of variable becomes v.
    «
        v Hist 1                 v will be ready to be added to result of
        «                           procedure: For each element in Hist,
            DUP v SAME              keep the element
            « DROP »               unless it matches v.
            IFT
        »
        DOLIST                   The DOLIST executes this procedure.
        +                        Now add v to front of resulting list
        'Hist' STO               Store this as updated Hist.
    »
»
```

Clear (# 44294d)

```
«
    0 'Angle' STO 0 'Base' STO        Set all variable values
    0 'Rise' STO 0 'Slope' STO           to zero.
    { Angle Base Rise Slope }         Set default Hist list;
    'Hist' STO CLEAR                     clear Stack.
»
```

Quit (# 41126d)   *(Assigned to* ⬅CONT *key.)*

```
«
    { 51.2 91.2 65 75 85 95 }              Delete key assignments;
    DELKEYS K STOKEYS                         restore previous keys
    F STOF                                    and flags.
    { F K Angle Base Rise Slope CST Hist }
    PURGE                                  Purge unneeded variables.
    HOME FIS 2 MENU                        Get VAR menu in FIS
»                                             directory.
```

&Go (# 43560d)

```
«
    RCLF 'F' STO RCLKEYS 'K' STO     Save flags, keys.
    4 FIX DEG -62 SF Clear           Set modes, variables.
    {
        Ft→FIS 51.2 Quit 91.2
        FISD 65 FISM 75 FISS 85 FISA 95
    }                                            Make key
    STOKEYS                                      assignments.
    {                                Begin specifying custom menu:
        {
            "ANGL"                   First item label.
            {
            « 'Angle' Calc »     Unshifted action (calculate).
            « 'Angle' Out »      ⬅-shifted action (store).
            « 'Angle' DUP RCL SWAP →TAG »  ➡-shifted
            }                        action (recall).
        }
        {
            "BASE"                   Next item label.
            {
            « 'Base' Calc »      Unshifted action (calculate).
            « 'Base' Out »       ⬅-shifted action (store).
            « 'Base' DUP RCL SWAP →TAG »  ➡-shifted
            }                        action (recall).
        }
        {
            "RISE"                   Next item label.
            {
            « 'Rise' Calc »      Unshifted action (calculate).
            « 'Rise' Out »       ⬅-shifted action (store).
            « 'Rise' DUP RCL SWAP →TAG »  ➡-shifted
            }                        action (recall).
        }
        {
            "SLOPE"                  Next item label.
            {
            « 'Slope' Calc »     Unshifted action (calculate).
            « 'Slope' Out »      ⬅-shifted action (store).
            « 'Slope' DUP RCL SWAP →TAG »  ➡-shifted
            }                        action (recall).
        }
        { "→Ft"   FIS→Ft } Clear  Last two menu items.
    }
    MENU                             Create the custom menu.
»
```

This **Calc** routine is the key to the equation-selection "smarts" of the solution. Essentially, it is just a large, nested **CASE** statement that determines which "known" value was updated *least* recently (the "oldest **Hist** item"—last in that list). It uses that determination to decide which routine(s) to employ to calculate the unknown value.

```
Calc (#  32871d)
   « DUP Hist 4 GET DUP ROT SAME    Get 4th (last) item in Hist.
     « DROP Hist 3 GET »               Or, if it matches given
     IFT                                name, get 3rd item.
     → u x                           Given name is u; oldest
     «                                  Hist item is x.
        CASE                         What are you solving for?
           u 'Angle' SAME           If solving for Angle,
           THEN                          then
                 CASE               What Hist item is oldest?
                    x 'Slope' SAME  If Slope is oldest,
                    THEN                find Angle via Base
                          A~BR           and Rise.
                    END
                    x 'Rise' SAME   If Rise is oldest,
                    THEN                find Rise via Base
                          R~BS A~BR     and Slope, then Angle
                    END                 via Base and Rise.
                    B~RS A~BR       Otherwise, find Base via
                 END                    Rise and Slope, then
           END                          Angle via Base & Rise.
           u 'Base' SAME            If solving for Base,
           THEN                          then
                 CASE               What Hist item is oldest?
                    x 'Slope' SAME  If Slope is oldest,
                    THEN                find Base via
                          B~AR          Angle and Rise.
                    END
                    x 'Rise' SAME   If Rise is oldest,
                    THEN                find Rise via Angle
                          R~AS B~AR     and Slope, then Base
                    END                 via Angle and Rise.
                    B~RS            Otherwise, find Base via
                 END                    Rise and Slope.
           END
        END
```

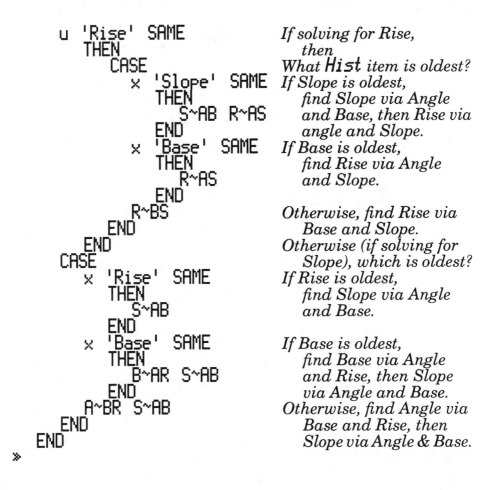

```
  u 'Rise' SAME              If solving for Rise,
    THEN                        then
        CASE                 What Hist item is oldest?
        x 'Slope' SAME       If Slope is oldest,
          THEN                  find Slope via Angle
              S~AB R~AS         and Base, then Rise via
          END                  angle and Slope.
        x 'Base' SAME        If Base is oldest,
          THEN                  find Rise via Angle
              R~AS             and Slope.
          END
        R~BS                 Otherwise, find Rise via
      END                       Base and Slope.
    END                      Otherwise (if solving for
  CASE                          Slope), which is oldest?
    x 'Rise' SAME            If Rise is oldest,
      THEN                      find Slope via Angle
          S~AB                  and Base.
      END
    x 'Base' SAME            If Base is oldest,
      THEN                      find Base via Angle
          B~AR S~AB             and Rise, then Slope
      END                       via Angle and Base.
      A~BR S~AB              Otherwise, find Angle via
    END                         Base and Rise, then
  END                           Slope via Angle & Base.
  »
»
```

A CASE statement structure is certainly not the only way to accomplish the equation selection task. You could instead use a set of (deeply) nested IF...THEN...ELSE clauses. Or, you could store the various trig programs within a list, and select from the list via a pointer. As with any program, there are many possibilities.

Memory Management Programs

This next project is a set you'll find many uses for—put it in your **HOME** directory: A set of tools for easily moving, copying, renaming, reordering, purging, and analyzing variables *and* directories. Namely, these:

{ *name1* *name2* ... **}** `Tidy`   *or*   `'` *name* `'` `Tidy`   *or*   `Tidy`
In the current directory, alphabetizes the given name(s) and all their subdirectories (directories alphabetize ahead of other names). Execution on an empty Stack (or empty list) tidies all names in the current VARS menu, but not in any of those names' subdirectories.

{ *name1* *name2* ... **}** `Bytes`   *or* `'` *name* `'` `Bytes`   *or*   `Bytes`
Sums the checksums and bytes of the named object(s). Execution on empty Stack sums all names in the current VAR menu.

{ *name1* *name2* ... **}** `Purge`   *or*   `'` *name* `'` `Purge`
Deletes all the given names from the current directory.

{ *name1* *name2* ... **}** **{** *destination path* **}** `Copy`
Copies all the given named objects from the current directory to the destination path. If such a path does not exist, it is created. A single name is also acceptable instead of a list.

{ *name1* *name2* ... **}** **{** *destination path* **}** `Move`
Performs a `Copy` and then `Purges` the original(s).

{ *old name1* *old name2* ... **}** **{** *new name1* *new name2* ...**}** `Rename`
In the current directory, renames all the given named objects. A single name is also acceptable instead of a list.

Tidy (# 9541d)

```
«
    DEPTH NOT « { } » IFT          If empty Stack, supply { }.
    °N→L PATH                      Ensure arg. is list; get path.
    → n P                          Argument list becomes n;
    «                              current path becomes P.
        n SIZE                     If arg. list is not empty,
        «                            keep a copy, and,
            n n 1                    for every element,
            «                        if it names a directory, move
                DUP VTYPE 15 ==         there & Tidy all its VARS
                « EVAL VARS Tidy »      (a recursive use of Tidy);
                « DROP »             if element does not name
                IFTE                   a directory, DROP it.
            »
            DOLIST
        »
        « VARS »                    If arg. list is empty, substitute
        IFTE                          VARS list.
        P EVAL 2 MENU               Return to original VAR menu.
        °VSep SORT SWAP SORT SWAP + Alphabetize arg. list
        DUP SIZE                             (directories first)
        « ORDER »                   If resulting list is non-empty,
        « DROP »                      ORDER it; otherwise, DROP
        IFTE                          it.
    »
»
```

Bytes (# 4586d)

```
«
    DEPTH NOT « VARS » IFT         If empty Stack, supply VARS.
    DUP TYPE 5 ==                  If argument is a list,
    «                                then
        DUP SIZE                    if it is not empty,
        «                            start running sums at 0;
            0 0 ROT 1                for every element in list,
            « BYTES ROT + 3 ROLLD + SWAP »  add its BYTES
            DOSUBS                   to the running sums.
        »
        « BYTES »                   If argument is empty list,
        IFTE                          run BYTES on that object.
    »
    « BYTES »                       If argument is not a list, do a
    IFTE                              normal BYTES function.
»
```

Purge (# 64251d)

```
«
    IF
        DUP SIZE          If arguments to be purged number at least 1,
    THEN
        ▫N→L              Convert single name to list, if necessary.
        ▫VSep             Separate arguments into lists of directories
        PURGE                and names; purge names list.
        DUP SIZE          If directories list is not empty,
        « PGDIR »            purge that list;
        « DROP »             otherwise drop that list.
        IFTE
    ELSE                  If original argument list is empty,
        DROP                 drop it.
    END
»
```

▫VSep (# 49659d)

```
«
    IF                        If list of arguments to be separated
        DUP SIZE                  is not empty,
    THEN
        DUP { } SWAP          Save copy of argument list; start
        1                        empty list to collect dir. names.
        «                    For every element in argument list,
            DUP VTYPE 15 ==      if type is directory
            « + »               add it to collection list;
            « DROP »            otherwise, drop it.
            IFTE
        »
        DOLIST               This command does the above.
        SWAP { } SWAP        Get other copy of argument list;
        1                        start another empty list.
        «                    Do exact same procedure
            DUP VTYPE 15 ≠       as above,
            « + »               but for non-directory
            « DROP »            elements.
            IFTE
        »
        DOLIST               This command does it all.
    ELSE                     If argument list was empty,
        DUP                      make two of them (to represent
    END                          lists of directories and names).
»
```

```
·N→L (# 2734d)
  «
      DUP TYPE 6 ==                    If argument is a name,
      « 1 →LIST »                         make it a list.
      IFT
  »


·ChkPth (# 63704d)
  «
      PATH                             Note current path.
      OVER                             Get copy of given dest. path.
      REVLIST OBJ→                     Reverse and put onto Stack.
      SWAP EVAL 1 -                    Go HOME—1 fewer path levels.
      WHILE                            While there are other path
          DUP 0 >                         levels to traverse,
      REPEAT
          SWAP DUP VTYPE -1 ==  If next level given is empty name,
          « DUP CRDIR »                   a directory by that name
          IFT                             needs to be created.
          IF                           If next level given truly is a
              DUP VTYPE 15 ==             directory now,
          THEN                         then
              EVAL                         move there;
          ELSE
              0 0 /                     otherwise generate an error.
          END
          1 -                          Decrement path level counter.
      END                              End of loop.
      DROP EVAL                        Drop counter and return to
  »                                       original path.


Copy (# 10321d)
  «
      0 ·Cpy                           Send "Copy" signal argument
  »                                       to underlying ·Cpy routine.


Move (# 27967d)
  «
      1 ·Cpy                           Send "Move" signal argument
  »                                       to underlying ·Cpy routine.
```

```
▪Cpy (# 46415d)
  «
      SWAP ROT ▪N→L ▪VSep          Clean up input argument.
      ROT ▪ChkPth                  Check/prepare destination path.
      PATH                         Note current path.
    → m d v t f                    m=move indic.; d=dir. list; v=var.
      «                               list; t=dest. path; f=curr. path.
        IF
          t f SAME NOT              If not copying to same directory,
        THEN                          then:
          IF
            v SIZE                  If variable list is not empty
          THEN                        then:
            v                       For every element
            1                          in that list,
            « RCL »                    recall its value.
            DOLIST                  Do this for entire list.
            t EVAL                  Move to destination directory.
            v                       For every corresponding element
            2                          pair in variable and values list,
            « STO »                    store the value in the name.
            DOLIST                  Do this for entire lists.
            f EVAL                  Move back to original path.
            m                       If m is non-zero, this indicates a
            « v PURGE »                move rather than a copy, so purge
            IFT                        original variable list.
          END                      End of treatment of variable list.
          IF
            d SIZE                  If directory list is not empty
          THEN                        then:
            t EVAL                  Move to destination directory.
            d CRDIR                 Create directories given in list.
            f EVAL                  Move back to original directory.
            d                       For every element
            1                          in directory list:
            «
              DUP EVAL              Move to that directory.
              VARS                  Get list of all its contents.
              t ROT +              Add dir. name to current destina-
              Copy                    tion path; do a Copy (recursive).
              f EVAL                 Move back to original directory.
            »
            DOLIST                  Do this for entire list.
            m                       If m is non-zero, this indicates a
            « d PGDIR »                move rather than a copy, so purge
```

```
      IFT                    original directory list.
    END                      End of treatment of directory list.
  END                        End of original IF statement.
»
»
```

Rename (# 28946d)

```
«
    ·N→L SWAP ·N→L                   Clean up input arguments.
    PATH                             Note current path.
    → n v h                          n=new names; v=curr. names;
    «                                    h=current path.
      IF                                 If v is not empty and
          v SIZE DUP n SIZE == AND   the sizes of v and n
      THEN                               match, then:
          n                        For every corresponding pair
          v                            of elements
          2                            in those two lists,
          «
          IF
              DUP VTYPE 15 ≠      If the v-element is not a dir.,
          THEN                       then
              DUP RCL                recall value;
              SWAP PURGE             purge old name;
              SWAP STO               store in new name.
          ELSE                   Otherwise (v-element is a dir.)
              SWAP DUP CRDIR         create dir. with new name;
              SWAP DUP EVAL          move to old-name directory;
              VARS ROT               get a list of its contents;
              h SWAP +               add new name to curr. path;
              Move                   Do a Move.
              UPDIR PGDIR            Go up to old-name's parent
          END                        and purge old-name dir.
          »
          DOLIST                   Do this for entirety of two lists.
      END                          End of original IF statement.
    »
»
```

Data Analysis Application: A Gradebook

This final example is quite a project—with lots of examples of input and output formatting: Starting in a new subdirectory of **HOME** (call it **Grds**), build a set of programs that will manage and calculate scores, grades and GPA's for a student's entire academic record—every assignment for every class, every term, every school.

If you think about for a moment, you'll see that the HP 48's directory structure is already perfectly suited for the job of organizing such data: At the highest level, it lists the academic record school-by-school; each school is its own subdirectory. Then you create subdirectories term-by-term within each school, course-by-course within each term, and item-by-item (i.e. any assignment or test) for each course.

That is ideal: Whenever possible, you should design an application to use already-existing tools and their general mechanics and assumptions. Such intuitive design saves you work in programming, and it saves the user time and grief when learning to use the finished program. Here, for example, given that you'll be using ordinary directories, note that you can simply employ your **Purge** and **Rename** tools, along with the built-in **CRDIR** to build and arrange most of the data structure. In fact, the only places where you'll need to program "something special" are down at the Courses and Items levels.

With that notion in mind, the editing and calculation tools should treat directory items much as you are used to doing with ordinary variables. For example, if you put the name of a directory (or item) on the Stack, then [EVAL] could evaluate it (calculate grade, GPA, etc.) and [←][EDIT] could edit it—just as you would expect. Here's one solution:

Init (# 59466d)

```
«
    HOME Grds                          Move to proper directory.
    RCLF '°F' STO                      Store current flags.
    RCLKEYS '°K' STO                   Store current keys.
    {                                  List
        ~~~~ ~~~~~ ~~~~~~                  of
        CSc CHrs CWt CGr                  variables
        Targ Hrs Pts Origin               to
    }                                     initialize.
    1
    « 0 SWAP STO »                     For every element, store a
    DOLIST                                0 in it.
    2 FIX -62 SF                       Set FIX 2 and USER mode.
    {                                  List
        UpDir 31.2 Quit 31.3              of
        Calc 33 Edit 52.2                 key
    }                                     assignments.
    STOKEYS                            Make the assignments.
    15 TVARS                           Get all directory names.
    {                                  List of desired
        ~~~~ ~~~~~ ~~~~~~                 menu items to follow
        Init Edit Calc Quit               all directory names.
    }                                  Add these lists and rearrange
    + ORDER                               the VARS menu with result.
    "CRDIR, Purge, Rename or trav.    Opening message to
    [EDIT] to edit. [EVAL] to calc.      remind user how
    [HOME] to Quit."                       things work.
    MSGBOX                             Send the message.
    2 MENU                             Be sure VARS menu is present.
»
```

Quit (# 34099d)   *(Assigned to →HOME key.)*

```
«
    HOME Grds                          Move to proper directory.
    { 31.2 31.3 33 52.2 } DELKEYS     Del. key assignments.
    °K STOKEYS °F STOF                 Restore previous keys and flags.
    {                                  List of
        ~~~~ ~~~~~ ~~~~~~ CSc CWt CHrs CGr   variables
        Targ Pts Hrs Origin °F °K CST        no longer
    }                                        needed.
    PURGE                              Purge those variables.
    HOME 2 MENU                        Go to HOME directory
»                                         and show its VAR menu.
```

UpDir (# 56857d)
```
«
    PATH SIZE 2 ==
    « Quit »
    « UPDIR 2 MENU »
    IFTE
»
```
(A substitute for built-in UPDIR—
assigned to the ⤶(UP) key)
If now at { HOME GRDS } level,
clean up and go HOME;
otherwise do a normal UPDIR
and go to VAR menu.

Here is the main **Edit** routine (assigned to the ⤶(EDIT) key):

Edit (# 34938d)
```
«
    IF
        PATH SIZE 4 <
    THEN
        "You may EDIT only a course or item."
        MSGBOX
    ELSE
        IF
            PATH SIZE 4 ==
        THEN
            DEPTH
            «
                DUP TYPE 6 ≠
                « N4 »
                « E4 »
                IFTE
            »
            « N4 »
            IFTE
        ELSE
            DEPTH
            «
                DUP TYPE 6 ≠
                « N5 »
                « E5 »
                IFTE
            »
            « N5 »
            IFTE
        END
    END
»
```
If above the Courses directory level,
remind user
with
error message.
Otherwise,
if now at
the Courses directory level,
if given an argument,

if it's not an existing name,
create & edit new course;
otherwise, edit the
course specified.

If not given an argument,
create & edit a new course.
If now at Items level,
if given an argument,

if it's not an existing name,
create & edit new item;
otherwise, edit the
item specified.

If not given an argument,
create & edit a new item.

N4 and N5 are the two routines that, respectively, create (and edit) a new course and a new item. (The 4 and the 5 refer to the PATH SIZE of the directory level at which each is appropriate.) Each routine simply creates and stores a new list of the appropriate data structure (a 3-object list or an 8-object list, with appropriate object types in each position), with default values and names. Note that while the routines begin at differing levels, each stores its list at the Item level.

N4 (# 11930d)

```
«
    'NEWC' DUP DUP          Create a new directory called NEWC
    CRDIR EVAL                 and move to that directory.
    {                       Build the default INFO list:
        "NEWC"                  the course name;
        NOVAL                   its default # of semester hours;
        { 90 80 70 60 }         its default course curve percentages.
    }
    'INFO' STO              Store this as INFO.
    UpDir                   Move back up to the Courses level.
    E4                      Edit NEWC's INFO ('NEWC' was
»                              still on Stack for E4's argument).
```

N5 (# 39904d)

```
«
    'NEWI'                  New item's default name (arg. for E5).
    {                       Build the default list for the new item:
        "NEWI"                  the course name;
        NOVAL                   its weight (%) in course;
        { 90 80 70 60 }         its curve %'s for item grading;
        NOVAL                   its default raw score;
        NOVAL                   its default total possible;
        NOVAL                   its % score;
        "P"                     its default grading basis;
        NOVAL                   its letter grade.
    }
    OVER STO               Store this as NEWI.
    E5                     Now edit NEWI.
»
```

The actual editing routines are just extensive uses of the INFORM command, followed by a storage of the new data in place of the old.

E4 (# 8353d)

```
«
    DUP EVAL
    "EDIT COURSE"
    {
        { "NAME" "TYPE COURSE NAME." 2 }
        { "HOURS" "ENTER COURSE SEMESTER HRS." 0 }
        { "CURVE" "ENTER MIN. % FOR {A B C D}." 5 }
    }
    { }
    'INFO' RCL DUP
    INFORM
    «
        DUP 'INFO' STO
        HEAD
        PATH HOME
        SWAP OBJ→
        SWAP EVAL
    »
    « DUP »
    IFTE
    UpDir DUP2
    IF
        SAME NOT
    THEN
        Rename
    ELSE
        DROP DROP
    END
»
```

Move to Items level in Course directory specified by argument name.
First INFORM argument is screen label.
Next is list of field labels, instructions, and data types
(just 3 fields in course INFO).
Use default field column configurations
Use existing data for reset values and default (input suggestion) values. Go.
If return argument is 1 (inputs OK'd), store new list as INFO; take its first object (the course name), and, to convert string to name, note current path, move HOME to use OBJ→ (so evaluation gives empty name), then return via path noted.
If return argument is 0 (inputs cancelled), DUP current crs. name (still on Stack).
Move to Course level, prepare name comparison.
If names are not the same,

rename course with new name;

otherwise, drop both names.

E5 (# 25660d)

```
«
    → t
    «
        "EDIT ITEM"
        {
            { "NAME" "TYPE ITEM NAME." 2 }
            { }
```

Item name argument becomes t.

First INFORM argument is screen label.
Next is list of field labels, instructions, and data types:
(name fld., followed by blank column)

```
{
    "WT%" "ENTER WEIGHT% OF ITEM IN CRS."
    0                (Item weight%-in-course field)
}
{
    "CURV" "ENTER MIN. % FOR {A B C D}."
    5                (Item curve field)
}
{ }                 (Two blank fields after that,
{ }                      to allow room for long list)
{ "SC" "ENTER ITEM RAW SCORE." 0 }
{ "TL" "ENTER TOTAL POSSIBLE." 0 }
{
    "%" "(PERCENT SCORE WILL BE COMPUTED.)"
    0                (Raw score, total-possible and
}                         % score fields).
{
    "P/G" "MARK IS GRADE OR % (G OR P)?"
    2                (Grade-basis indicator field)
}
{ "GRD" "TYPE LETTER GRADE." 2 }(Grade field)
}
```

Code	Annotation
`{ 3 1 }`	Column numbering and spacing.
`t RCL DUP`	Use existing data for reset values and
`INFORM`	default (input suggestion) values. Go.
`«`	If return argument is 1 (inputs OK'd),
`DUP t STO`	store new list under name in t;
`HEAD`	take its first object (the item name),
`PATH HOME`	and, to convert string to name, note
`SWAP OBJ→`	current path, move **HOME** to use OBJ→
`SWAP EVAL`	(so evaluation gives empty name), then
`»`	return via path noted.
`« t »`	If return argument is 0 (inputs cancelled),
`IFTE`	supply second copy of name in t.
`t SWAP DUP2`	Prepare for names comparison.
`IF`	
`SAME NOT`	If names are not the same,
`THEN`	
`Rename`	rename item with new name;
`ELSE`	
`DROP DROP`	otherwise, drop both names.
`END`	
`»`	
`»`	

```
Calc (# 32285d)                    (Assigned to the [EVAL] key)
«                                  Flag 1 tells ▪Clc to note argument
    1 SF                               on first level of recursion only.
    PATH 'Origin' Sto              Note original path as Origin.
    0 'Pts' Sto 0 'Hrs' Sto        Start running sums at 0.
    ▪Clc                           Calculate (▪Clc calls itself as nec.)
    Targ                           Supply argument list or name.
    IF
        Origin SIZE 5 <            If at Courses level or higher,
    THEN
        Pts "Total Pts" →TAG       output gives total points,
        Hrs "Total Hrs" →TAG           total hours,
        DUP2 / "GPA" →TAG              and GPA.
    ELSE                           otherwise (if at Items level),
        CSc "Course %" →TAG        output gives combine % of arg.
        CGr "Course Grade" →TAG    items and equivalent grade.
    END
    Origin EVAL                    Return to original directory.
»


▪Clc (# 28704d)                    (The core calculation routine—
«                                      recursive.)
    IF
        DEPTH                      If the Stack is not empty,
    THEN
        DUP TYPE 6 ==              if the argument is a single name,
        « 1 →LIST »                    make it a list;
        «
            IF                     otherwise,
                DUP TYPE 5 ≠           if it's not a list,
            THEN
                GetAll                 get all VARS (except INFO).
            END
        »
        IFTE
    ELSE                           If the Stack is empty,
        GetAll                         get all VARS (except INFO).
    END
    1 FS?C                         If flag 1 is set, this is the first call of
    « DUP 'Targ' Sto »                 ▪Clc—note arg. list as Targ;
    IFT                                clear the flag regardless.
    → t                            The argument list becomes t.
    «
        IF
```

```
      t SIZE                          If t is not empty,
THEN
   IF
      PATH SIZE 5 <                    if above Items level,
      THEN                               for every element in
         t 1                             t, move to that sub-
         « EVAL GetAll "Clc »           dir., get all VARS
         DOLIST                         but INFO and "Clc.
      ELSE                             If not above Items level,
         0 0 0 'CHrs' Sto               initialize course
         'CSc' Sto 'CWt' Sto            running sums;
         t 1                            for each elem. in t,
         «
            → n                          element is n;
            «
               IF
                  n 7 GET "G" ==        If n's grade basis
               THEN                       is letter, get
                  n 8 GET  INFO 3 GET    grd. & crs. crv.,
                  G→P n 6 ROT PUT        find % & store.
               ELSE                     If n is %-based gr.,
                  n 4 GET n 5 GET         get raw score &
                  / 100 * DUP            total, find &
                  n 6 ROT PUT            store %, calc. &
                  n 3 GET P→G            store corresp.
                  n 8 ROT PUT            letter grade;
               END
               n 2 GET 100 / DUP DUP    add n's weight
               'CWt' StoPl              to crs. wt. sum;
               n 6 GET *                add weighted
               SWAP INFO 2 GET *        score & hours
               'CHrs' StoPl             to those course
               'CSc' StoPl             sums.
            »
         »
         DOLIST                        All elements totalled;
         CSc CWt / DUP 'CSc' Sto       normalize crs. score;
         INFO 3 GET P→G DUP 'CGr' Sto    find crs. grd.
         { 75 50 25 0 } G→P 25 /       via curve & add
         INFO 2 GET SWAP OVER *        resulting grade
         'Pts' StoPl 'Hrs' StoPl       points and hours
      END                              to overall running
END                                    sums.
   »
»
```

GetAll (# 38093d)   *(Get all VARS except **INFO**)*

```
«
    IF
        PATH SIZE 5 ==          If now at Items level,
    THEN
        VARS DUP                get all VARS;
        'INFO' POS              find where INFO is in that list;
        → V P                   list=V; INFO's position=P;
        «
            V 1 P 1 - SUB       extract all of list prior to p;
            V P 1 + V SIZE SUB  extract all of list after p;
            +                   combine the two extractions.
        »
    ELSE                        If not at Items level, get all directory
        15 TVARS                names only.
    END
»
```

G→P (# 6014d)   *(Convert letter grade to percentage)*

```
«
    OBJ→ DROP                   Decompose list of curve percentages.
    → g b c d f                 Grade=g; min. "A"=max. "B"=b;
    «                           likewise for c, d and f.
        CASE
            g NUM 65 ==         If first character in g is "A",
            THEN
                100             percentage is 100;
            END
            g NUM 66 ==         if first character in g is "B",
            THEN
                b               percentage is b;
            END
            g NUM 67 ==         if first character in g is "C",
            THEN
                c               percentage is c;
            END
            g NUM 68 ==         if first character in g is "D",
            THEN
                d               percentage is d;
            END
            f                   otherwise, percentage is f.
        END
    »
»
```

```
P→G (# 57069d)                    (Convert percentage to letter grade)

   «
      OBJ→ DROP                    Decompose list of curve %'s.
      → p a b c d                  Percentage=p; min. "A"=a; min
      «                               "B"=b; likewise for c, d and f.
         CASE
            p a ≥                  If percentage is ≥ a ,
               THEN
                  "A"                 grade is "A";
               END
            p a < p b ≥ AND        if a > percentage ≥ b,
               THEN
                  "B"                 grade is "B";
               END
            p b < p c ≥ AND        if b > percentage ≥ c,
               THEN
                  "C"                 grade is "C";
               END
            p c < p d ≥ AND        if c > percentage ≥ d,
               THEN
                  "D"                 grade is "D";
               END
            "F"                    otherwise, grade is "F".
         END
      »
   »
```

```
Sto (# 15013d)                    (A substitute for built-in STO—
   «                                  stores into { HOME GRDS }).
      PATH 3 ROLLD                 Note current path above other args.
      HOME Grds STO                Move to { HOME GRDS } and STO.
      EVAL                         Go back to original directory.
   »
```

```
StoPl (# 3915d)                   (A substitute for built-in STO+—
   «                                  stores into { HOME GRDS }).
      PATH 3 ROLLD                 Note current path above other args.
      HOME Grds STO+               Move to { HOME GRDS } and STO+.
      EVAL                         Go back to original directory.
   »
```

More Ideas

Of course, one book can never contain more than a few of the myriad possibilities for useful programs on the HP 48. For example, here are a few projects that, due to space limitations, didn't make it into this book. The strategies are outlined (but you may think of better ways). Tackle them as you wish; you will learn a lot—and enjoy the challenge!

Other Data Analysis Applications

After working through the gradebook example, you can now see some of the possibilities of the HP 48 as a general data analysis application driver. Using the same basic strategy as the gradebook example, you could construct similar applications for a variety of relevant topics.

For example, recall the description of the static free-body analysis on page 243: You could create your list of forces and moments via `INFORM`. And the whole application could live in a directory structure like this: `{ HOME FREEB WORK DATA }` As usual, the first level of subdirectory, `FreeB` would contain the program routines themselves; and `Work` would be the level from which you'd execute them. But the program would name and store the free-body descriptor lists at the `Data` level— safe from "clobbering" from the `Work` level.

Of course, that is just one of many areas for this general application pattern. You could do something similar for circuits, chemical equations, statistics, and on and on. *Use what you've already seen and done* —not in the details (those are different for every topic) but in the strategies for how the program to works with the user, store data, etc.

Alternative Calculator: A Vector Calculator with Units

Another general programming pattern to consider is the extension or modification of the calculator's basic arithmetic and number-crunching capabilities.

For example, you could write a set of routines to allow your HP 48 to do common arithmetic with vectors (and real numbers) that may have units attached. All object types would appear and behave normally, except that a list is assumed to be a vector with units, in this format: { [1 2 3] 1_m}.

The arithmetic keys would be reassigned to handle this special format when it is encountered. Those arithmetic routines would also judge when ⊠ should mean CROSS and ⟋ should mean DOT. Also, for convenience, you could assign →V2 and →V3 to ←ENTER and →ENTER, respectively, and the RAD/DEG and RECT/CYLIN/SPHER commands to other convenient keys. Then you could offer custom menus of unit selectors that behave like the built-in units menus but also accept vector arguments (formatting them, as necessary, into the list notation).

Directory recommendation: { HOME VECS WORK } Vecs is where you store all the programs; Work is the subdirectory from which you use them and in which you can store results of your calculations without worrying about name conflicts with your routines. (And don't forget to do a cleanup routine, as well as your setup routine.)

(For another, more involved example of altering your calculator's basic functionality, consider the following idea, too. --->   )

Alternative Calculator: Significant-Figures, with Units

Write a set of routines to allow your HP 48 to do normal Stack operations and arithmetic (including units), where each real or unit value
is retained internally (on the Stack) in full machine precision, but
where only its significant figures (and units, if any) are displayed.

This task has several problems. The first problem is to decide how to
carry, with the value itself, its precision information—i.e., how many
of its digits are significant. You could opt for a list format —containing
the value, its precision, and its units—similar to the vector calculator
described on the previous page. But that's too much visual clutter
around what should be an easy-to-read value in the display. (By contrast, since vectors are long, often multiple-line objects anyway, the
attaching of units via lists isn't such a major detraction there).

Consider this: Suppose that you round the last digit in each value's
mantissa and substitute a precision digit (0-9), that indicates how
many decimal places are significant in the mantissa. That way you
have up to 10 digits (9 decimal places) of accuracy, plus a guard digit
by which to round, plus your precision digit—all in one value.

The second problem is to decide on a readable way to format the significant digit display of the value. A list is too ugly, but how about a tag?
Suppose that you set the display to single line mode (i.e. non-multi-line
mode) and format the entire significant portion of the value—including its unit—as a string, then use that to tag the value itself. If you're
clever in how you pad that string, the value itself (with its embedded
precision and its unit, if any) will be preserved but will disappear out
to the right (off the screen); you'll see only the significant part—the tag.

Notice that the tag strategy is appropriate also in that a tag disappears when you do anything to the value—which is exactly when the tag must change anyway, since the precision of the result may be different.

The third problem is how to emulate normal Stack operations otherwise. You could generally ignore this question with the vector calculator because the mechanics of keying in a vector are a little more involved than for real numbers. Vector arithmetic is much more limited than for real numbers, anyway. But the convenience of this program diminishes if you need to change a lot of "driving habits" just to do simple arithmetic. And you don't want to use custom menus here; you may need the built-in real-number and UNITS menus.

Suggestion: Try *vectored ENTER*. Any Stack-oriented command you execute manually (via a key) generally does an "implied ENTER" (i.e. puts the Command Line onto the Stack) first. But when flags -62 (**USER**) and -63 (vectored ENTER) are both set, the rules are different:

- First, *if* the name αENTER exists, the Command Line is put onto the Stack as a *string* and αENTER is evaluated.

- Next, the command itself is executed.

- Then, *if* the name βENTER exists, the command name itself is put onto the stack as a string and βENTER is evaluated.

This gives you a way both to test what was on the command line (therefore how to treat it) and what command was executed (therefore what to do about it or how to reformat the result afterwards). Have fun!

Recommendations: Use { HOME SIGF WORK } as a directory structure (similar to the vector calculator). And you should probably build/purge αENTER and βENTER in your setup/cleanup routines.

Dead-Reckoning Course and Speed

For you navigation buffs, here's more practice with the EquationWriter, formatted numbers, custom menus, and/or the Solver: Write a set of routines that, when given a set of destination coordinates (longitude and latitude, in DD.MMSS format), will compute some combination of following: Course and speed of travel, net course and speed of ambient conditions (wind and/or current), estimated time of arrival.

Here are some relevant facts:*

$$\cos(GCD) = \sin(Lat_1)\sin(Lat_2) + \cos(Lat_1)\cos(Lat_2)\cos|Lng_1 - Lng_2|$$

$$\cos(Z) = \sin(Lat_2) - \cot(GCD)\sin(Lat_1)\cos(Lat_1)$$

In these equations, *GCD* is the Great Circle Distance, expressed in arc; *Z* is the Great Circle initial heading, in degrees.

Strategy 1: Create a solution (similar to the first FIS triangle program example) where a custom menu mimics a VAR menu and judges which equation to use by which values were modified most recently.

Strategy 2: Create a list of linked Solver equations, where you rotate the appropriate equation in and out of the Solver, as needed. Note that you can't add any frills (conversion routines) to the menu, though.

Strategy 3: Make a MES (Multiple Equation Solution), where the Solver is smart enough to know which variables it has enough information to solve for. Note that you can't add any frills to the menu, though.

*Acknowledgments: These formulas are described in *The Sailings*, a public-domain program originally written for the HP-41 by Derrill M. Daniel. In turn, Mr. Daniel makes reference to The Calculator Afloat, a fascinating book by Captain Henry H. Shufeldt and Kenneth E. Newcommer, Naval Institute Press, Annapolis, MD.

3-D Topographical Analysis and Plotting

One thing you may have noticed about the 3-D plotting and analysis tools in the HP 48: They generally require a mathematical function, $z = f(x,y)$ to generate the points. If you have a set of raw empirical data (say, readings from a topographical survey), you'll need some tools to help you sort, analyze and visualize it. Write some: Assume that the data appears in a matrix of n rows by 3 columns, where each row represents a single point. The first column is the northing coordinate; the second column is the easting; the final column is the altitude.

Your first mission is to sort the matrix by northing, then by easting, so that the points appear in the matrix as they would have been recorded if a surveyor traversed over the grid in an orderly fashion—back and forth, as if mowing a lawn. Then, offer some data visualization:*

- Provide a routine that will use a bar plot to show any one cross-sectional slice (E-W or N-S) of the landscape in question.

- Provide a "fly-through" routine that animates the entire set of those cross-sectional slices—again, either E-W or N-S.

- Provide a perspective panorama (i.e. a view looking somewhat down at an angle on the landscape). Hint: Combine successively modulated slices via GXOR.

- Animate the perspective as a "flyover" routine.

Directory recommendation: **{ HOME TOPO WORK }** (with approach and reasoning similar to the vectors problem on page 279.)

---

*If graphics solutions are of special interest, you may want to read <u>Graphics on the HP 48G/GX</u>, by Ray Depew. See the back of this book for more information.

Cincinnati 5-Way Tic-Tac-Toe

Life just wouldn't be complete without a game or two. Writing your own game program on the HP 48 can get very involved, of course, depending upon what game you choose. In fact, it's one of the harder questions to answer: What game and with what rules?

Here's a simple first try (and it's hard enough): Write a set of routines to play a modified version of tic-tac-toe on the screen of your HP 48. Make the playing area a 15 x 15 grid of squares (with each square a 4 x 4 block of pixels). The object of the game is just like regular tic-tac-toe, but you must get *five* in a row (vertically, horizontally or diagonally)—not just three. Simple game, but quite interesting.

Obviously you're one player, but see if you can allow the other player to be either another humanoid (easier) or the machine itself (harder). Allow the players to choose who is X and who is O, and who goes first. It also might be nice to show either in the menu or the display (on either side of the board) whose turn it is.

Don't forget to allow an edit/correction routine in case a player fumble-fingers his/her move to the wrong location and wants to undo it (ah, but no changes after the other player has made his/her next move)!

Directory recommendation: **{ HOME TTTX5 PLAY }** This structure is similar in scheme and rationale to the vector calculator example on page 279.

---

*Again, if graphics-oriented programs are of special interest, you may want to read <u>Graphics on the HP 48G/GX</u>, by Ray Depew. See the back of this book for more information.

As you can tell from these ideas and examples, sometimes thinking through the strategies and writing little "warm-up" routines —parts of larger programs—can help you focus on what the real problems are.

Often the hardest part is not the actual core calculation but rather how to make it easily accessible without compromising the convenience of the rest of the machine. With so many tools to interact with, a program's design and compatibility is as important as the results it produces. It pays to "sit on your hands" or play on paper a bit before rushing into much of the program code itself.

Then, when you do begin to the code, try not to go overboard the other way: Learning never really stops, and with a machine like the HP 48, your "tinkering" could go on indefinitely. Programming is addictive, and it's all too easy to lose sight of the reason you began a program in the first place. You will *always* be able to find other ways to solve any problem (including those presented here)—more clearly, quickly or elegantly.

So, one of the most important (and most difficult) lessons to learn about programming is *when to stop*. If you do it as a hobby, that's one thing—then it's just a pastime. But if you do it to build a tool for a necessary task, you should keep one question firmly in mind:

"Has the extra time I am spending to improve this program begun to outweigh the added benefit I thereby gain when using it?"

Hopefully, these pages will help you often to answer: "Not yet."

Foundation Completed

This is only the beginning—truly just a foundation of understanding—upon which you should continue to build and use your 48 workshop.

As you certainly realize by now, there's no way that any single book could give you an in-depth look at everything about the 48. You probably noticed on many occasions that this Course made just a passing, one-time reference to a certain function, keystrokes or calculation method. It was by necessity, not by neglect.

So if you marked those spots or scratched your head over them, you might wish now to read some of the books recommended on pages 164-165—to explore some of those "breezed-over" features.

Note also that this Course did not cover:

- Alarms and the TIME application;
- Printing;
- Transferring data into and out of the 48;
- Using plug-in cards;
- Using the LIBRARY features;
- Making backup objects; the ARCHIVE command.

Those topics are best handled by your HP User's Guide.

Index

Reader Comments

We here at Grapevine like to hear feedback about our books. It helps us produce books tailored to your needs. If you have any specific comments or advice for our authors after reading this book, we'd appreciate hearing from you!

Which of our books do you have?

Comments, Advice and Suggestions:

May we use your comments as testimonials?

Your Name: Profession:

City, State:

How long have you had your calculator?

Please send Grapevine catalogs to these persons:

Name _____

Address _____

City _____ State _____ Zip _____

Name _____

Address _____

City _____ State _____ Zip_____

Here are some other related Grapevine books (see also pp. 164-165):

Graphics on the HP 48G/GX

Here's a "must-have" if you want to use the full potential of that big display. Ray Depew shows you how to build graphics objects ("grobs") and how to use them to program and customize displays with diagrams, pictures, and data plots. First the book offers a great in-depth review of the built-in graphics tools. Then you learn to build your own grobs and use them in programs—with impressive results!

Algebra/Pre-Calculus on the HP 48G/GX

Calculus on the HP 48G/GX

Grab your calculator, grab this book, and you're all set for math class. You'll get lots of lessons, examples and advice on graphing and problem-solving with:

Functions (linear, quadratic, rational, polynomial), trig, coordinate and analytic geometry, conics, equations of lines and planes, inequalities, vectors.

You'll also get great programmed tricks and tips for plotting and solving—all from an experienced classroom math teacher.

Get ready now for your college math! Plot and solve problems with this great collection of lessons, examples and program tricks from an experienced classroom math teacher:

Limits, series, sums, vectors and gradients, differentiation (formal, stepwise, implicit, partial), integration (definite, indefinite, improper, by parts, with vectors), rates, curve shapes, function averages, constraints, growth & decay, force, velocity, acceleration, arcs, surfaces of revolution, solids, and more.

The HP 48G/GX Pocket Guide

Don't take your calculator anywhere without this handy quick-reference booklet! *It fits right in the case with your HP 48G/GX*, and it's packed with the reminders you need most: The alpha keyboard; object types/syntax; constants/reserved names; names, variables, directories and paths; menus, diagrams and summaries; custom menus/key assignments; system flags; and *a complete command index*.

For more details on these or any of our books, check with your local bookseller or electronics dealer. For a full Grapevine catalog, write, call or fax:

Grapevine Publications, Inc.
626 N.W. 4th Street   P.O. Box 2449
Corvallis, Oregon   97339-2449   U.S.A.
Phone: 1-800-338-4331 *or* 541-754-0583
Fax: 541-754-6508

ISBN		Price*
	Books for personal computers	
0-931011-28-0	**Lotus** Be Brief	$ 9.95
0-931011-29-9	A Little **DOS** Will Do You	9.95
0-931011-32-9	Concise and **WordPerfect**	9.95
0-931011-37-X	An Easy Course in Using **WordPerfect**	19.95
0-931011-38-8	An Easy Course in Using **LOTUS 1-2-3**	19.95
0-931011-40-X	An Easy Course in Using **DOS**	19.95
	Books for Hewlett-Packard Scientific Calculators	
0-931011-18-3	An Easy Course in Using the **HP-28S**	9.95
0-931011-25-6	**HP-28S** Software Power Tools: **Electrical Circuits**	9.95
0-931011-26-4	An Easy Course in Using the **HP-42S**	19.95
0-931011-27-2	**HP-28S** Software Power Tools: **Utilities**	9.95
0-931011-33-7	**HP 48S/SX** Graphics	19.95
0-931011-XX-0	**HP 48S/SX** Machine Language	19.95
0-931011-41-8	An Easy Course in Using and Programming the **HP 48G/GX**	19.95
0-931011-42-6	Graphics on the **HP 48G/GX**	19.95
0-931011-43-4	Algebra/Pre-Calculus on the **HP 48G/GX**	19.95
0-931011-44-2	Calculus on the **HP 48G/GX**	19.95
0-931011-45-0	The **HP 48G/GX** Pocket Guide	9.95
0-931011-46-9	The **HP 38G** Pocket Guide	9.95
	Books for Hewlett-Packard financial calculators	
0-931011-08-6	An Easy Course in Using the **HP-12C**	19.95
0-931011-12-4	The **HP-12C Pocket Guide:** Just In Case	6.95
0-931011-19-1	An Easy Course in Using the **HP 19Bɪɪ**	19.95
0-931011-20-5	An Easy Course In Using the **HP 17Bɪɪ**	19.95
0-931011-22-1	The **HP 19Bɪɪ Pocket Guide:** Just In Case	6.95
0-931011-23-X	The **HP 17Bɪɪ Pocket Guide:** Just In Case	6.95
0-931011-XX-0	**Business Solutions** on Your HP Financial Calculator	9.95
	Books for Hewlett-Packard computers	
0-931011-35-3	**The Answers You Need** for the **HP 95LX**	9.95
0-931011-38-8	An Easy Course in Using **LOTUS 1-2-3**	19.95
0-931011-40-X	An Easy Course in Using **DOS**	19.95
	Other books	
0-931011-14-0	**Problem-Solving Situations:** A Teacher's Resource Book	9.95
0-931011-39-6	**House-Training Your VCR:** A Help Manual for Humans	9.95

Contact: **Grapevine Publications, Inc.**
626 N.W. 4th Street   P.O. Box 2449   Corvallis, Oregon   97339-2449   U.S.A.
800-338-4331 (541-754-0583)   *Fax:* 541-754-6508

*Prices shown are as of 8/6/96 and are subject to change without notice. Check with your
local bookseller or electronics/computer dealer—or contact Grapevine Publications, Inc.